GROWING PASTURES IN THE SOUTH

GROWING PASTURES IN THE SOUTH

BY

JOSEPH F. COMBS, B.S.
Pasture Crop Specialist
For seventeen years Agricultural Extension Agent
United States Department of Agriculture
and A. & M. College of Texas

CHAPEL HILL
The University of North Carolina Press

SECOND PRINTING, 1946
THIRD PRINTING, 1947
FOURTH PRINTING, 1948
FIFTH PRINTING, 1948
SIXTH PRINTING, 1948

MANUFACTURED IN THE UNITED STATES OF AMERICA
BY THE VAN REES PRESS, NEW YORK

Preface

BETTER pastures and grazing lands in the South will greatly aid in bringing about a more profitable and enduring type of agriculture. Nature has brought together the things that make it possible to develop the South into one of the greatest agricultural regions in the world, namely, temperate climate, fertile soil, and abundant rainfall. All these combine to insure successful pasture work, where adapted varieties of plants and correct methods of cultivation are used.

Improved pastures can be made to aid greatly in overcoming the disastrous one-crop system of many southern communities. Grazing crops could profitably occupy the lands from which our great forests of virgin timber have been removed. By sodding these areas, pasture crops will aid in saving the millions of acres of top soils that are being lost from erosion. These crops in turn will provide the background for improved livestock, self-sustaining farms, and a contented rural life.

This book is sent forth with the hope that it may be the means of creating a greater interest in the important program of pasture improvement, and that it may furnish reliable information on how to develop pasture areas into profitable grazing lands. The author has undertaken to assemble the recommendations of experts throughout the South, based on experimental data, and to combine them with his own personal observations over a period of many years.

The author wishes to acknowledge his indebtedness to Dr. A. J. Pieters, senior agronomist, Bureau of Plant Industry, Washington, D. C., for valuable assistance and for supplying many of the illustrations; to members of his staff, Messrs. H. N. Vinall, L. W. Kephart, Roland McKee and E. Marion Brown, for helpful suggestions; and to Mrs. Agnes Chase for supplying pictures of the paspalums.

He also wishes to acknowledge the assistance given by a number of experiment stations and Extension Service specialists, as cited; the help of Mr. Eugene Butler, editor of *The Progressive Farmer,* and Mr. Frank A. Briggs, editor, and Mr. T. C. Richardson, associate editor, of *Farm and Ranch,* for their critical assistance in connection with the subject matter of the book; and the cooperation of Mr. L. A. Schlup and members of the Extension Service staff in Washington for supplying many of the illustrations.

JOSEPH F. COMBS

Beaumont, Texas
March, 1936

Contents

GROWING PASTURES IN THE SOUTH

Chapter I

THE IMPORTANCE AND VALUE OF PASTURES

Introduction.—Pastoral industries were the first to engage the attention of civilized man, and today they hold an important place among the industries of all the great nations of the earth. The great grazing regions, including the steppes of Russia, the pampas of Brazil, the plains of Argentina and the vast pasture lands of Australia and New Zealand combine with the plains and mountain slopes of the United States to supply a large part of the beef, wool and other animal products that enter into the commerce of the nations.

In the South, grazing crops supply less than half the feed required for the production of the animal products of this region, although the southern states are well adapted to the production of pasture crops, because of the temperate climate, abundant rainfall and long growing season.

The South offers a great opportunity for the development of the dairy and beef cattle industry. Thousands of acres of land have been devoted to cotton production when they might have shown a greater net return from pastures, and at the same time contributed to the building of an industry that would have meant a more permanent agriculture in this section. The livestock industry of the

South will be expanded and improved only when the people recognize the potential value of good pastures.

Pasture Crops and Civilization.—Cattle, sheep and goats became domesticated animals in a very early period of our civilization. They have been the most important factors in providing food and raiment for those branches of the human race that have made the greatest progress. The value of pastures was recognized by the less civilized peoples in the early dawn of history. Their herds and flocks were moved from place to place in search of luxuriant pastures, and even at our present advanced stage of civilization this practice is still common in the sparsely settled regions of the world. In the more densely populated regions, farmers and stockmen recognize the necessity of providing their own pastures, where their improved herds may have access to nutritious grazing at all times without the necessity and expense of transferring them from place to place.

Permanent and Supplemental Pastures.—As referred to in this work, a permanent pasture is one located upon land not to be cultivated; and one which is used for grazing livestock over an indefinite period; planted to perennial, biennial or annual plants, or a combination thereof. Plantings of pasture crops on uncultivated lands to be used for the grazing of livestock over an indefinite period of time must be of such a nature as to endure continuous grazing and seasonal weather changes, with the ability to reseed or to come back from the roots from year to year, without the necessity of planting every year to prevent them from disappearing from the pasture.

A supplemental pasture is one located upon cultivated land, and planted to quick growing crops to be used for short periods of grazing. Temporary or supplemental

A Grazing Scene in the South. *Courtesy of Texas Agricultural Experiment Station.* Fig. 1.

pastures are used either in summer or winter. The quick growing crops planted on them are of such nature as to supply a maximum of forage in the shortest possible time. Crops on supplemental pastures are usually annuals, and are planted from year to year; however, biennials and perennials, such as sweet clover and alfalfa, are frequently used.

The Value of Pastures.—Good pastures make it possible for a farmer to keep more livestock on the farm without depending upon grain and forage crops from cultivated fields for their feed. Good pasture crops require no cultivation and are harvested by the animals themselves.

Improved pastures and improved livestock go hand in hand. Both are necessary to profitable production of beef, wool and animal products. The pasture should be considered an essential part of the farm. Its value should be recognized, and it should occupy a place of importance in the farm program and be made to return a large part of the farm receipts. Lands utilized for pastures have been undervalued. No system of farming can be considered permanently sound that does not include livestock, and good pastures form the basis of economical livestock production.

In 1930 a pasture of seven and one-half acres at the Iberia Livestock Experiment Farm, Jeanerette, Louisiana, grazed by six yearling Hereford grade cattle, produced gains of 1177 pounds. At the market price for this class of cattle at the time of the experiment, the return was equal to $12.62 per acre. In 1931 this same pasture with six head of cattle gave a gain of 173 pounds per acre, or a total of 1308 pounds. This pasture had no fertilizer, and no seed was ever sown on it. The crops consisted of

Registered Guernsey Calves on Improved Pasture, Darlington County, South Carolina. *Courtesy of Extension Service, United States Department of Agriculture.* Fig. 2.

White Dutch clover, Dallis and carpet grass. An adjoining pasture treated with pulverized oyster shells and two hundred pounds of superphosphate to the acre produced 245 pounds of gain per acre.

In dairy grazing experiments at the above mentioned station, the average return in feed value per acre for a period of three years was $67.38 per acre, where no fertilizer was applied; and $83.31 per acre where annual applications of two hundred pounds of superphosphate per acre were applied. While these experiments were in progress, the cows stayed on the pasture from early spring until late fall, and were wholly dependent upon the pasture for all their feed. The returns per acre in the dairy grazing experiments were based on a price of thirty-three cents per pound for butterfat.

Records were kept on eleven small pasture plots at Baton Rouge, Louisiana, during the pasture seasons of 1930 and 1931. Table I shows the yield of dry matter, area required to support one cow, and the period of growth. It will be noted that the yields are very high on these tests. This is largely due to the generous rainfall and fertile soil. The predominating pasture grasses were Dallis, Bermuda and crab grass. After the White Dutch clover slowed up, these grasses came on to hold up the high yields.

The total acre yield of dry matter for the 1930 season was 9,463 pounds, sufficient for 391 cow-days. The 1931 season showed a total acre yield of dry matter of 10,124 pounds, or enough for 418 cow-days.

In contrast with the Baton Rouge experiments, the Iberia Livestock Experiment Station, Jeanerette, Louisiana, clipped four plots at regular intervals during the season of 1931. These varied in size from 1.19 acres to

Grade Steers on Experimental Pasture, Iberia Livestock Experiment Farm, Jeanerette, Louisiana. Fig. 3.

TABLE I

The yield of dry matter per acre per day, and the estimated carrying capacity of clover and grass pasture clipped at monthly intervals at Baton Rouge, La. (Average of 4 plots in 1930, and 7 plots in 1931.)*

1930			1931		
Period of growth	*Dry matter per acre per day*	*Area required to support one milking cow*	*Period of growth*	*Dry matter per acre per day*	*Area required to support one milking cow*
	POUNDS	ACRES		POUNDS	ACRES
Feb. 10 † to Apr. 29	32.4	0.7	Feb. 10 † to Mar. 5.	49.1	0.5
Apr. 29 to May 29	35.5	0.7	Mar. 5 to Apr. 6	40.9	0.6
May 29 to July 11	41.4	0.6	Apr. 6 to May 5	56.0	0.4
July 11 to Aug. 11	41.3	0.6	May 5 to June 4	39.0	0.6
Aug. 11 to Sept. 11	58.3	0.4	June 4 to July 16	21.3	1.1
Sept. 11 to Oct. 13	31.5	0.8	July 16 to Aug. 14	62.1	0.4
			Aug. 14 to Sept. 15	42.8	0.6
			Sept. 15 to Oct. 29	18.8	1.3

* Table and experimental data supplied by R. H. Lush, La. Agr. Exp. Sta.

† Growth assumed to start February 10. The last day of each period of growth represents the clipping date.

1.69 acres. Plots 3A and 4A were clipped every 21 days, and plots 3B and 4B were clipped every 28 days. The principal pasture plants in these plots were White Dutch clover, Dallis grass, Bermuda grass, carpet grass and Vasey grass. The White Dutch clover was the predominating plant during the early part of the season.

The precipitation in inches by months for the season of 1930 at the Jeanerette Station was as follows: March, 4.71; April, 1.17; May, 2.39; June, 2.02; July, 5.48; August, 6.07; September, 3.36; and October, 3.33. Table II shows the yields of dry matter per acre per day, and the carrying capacity of the four plots estimated from the amount of dry matter. The total yield of dry matter per acre for plot 3A was 1,303 pounds, or sufficient for 56 cow-days; the yield of plot 4A was 1,536 pounds, sufficient for 66 cow-days; plot 3B, 1,588 pounds, sufficient for 68 cow-days; plot 4B, 1,769 pounds, sufficient for 76 cow-days. This shows an average of 66 cow-days per acre. The seasonal growth of the grass on the four plots, dry matter basis, is shown in Table II.

A grazing test was conducted in 1933 at the South Carolina Agricultural Experiment Station to determine the value of established Bermuda pasture. Three two-acre pastures were used in this test. Pastures No. 1 and No. 2, which had been in cultivation previous to 1930, received an application of 3000 pounds of dolomitic limestone per acre in the spring of 1931 and were continuously grazed in 1932. In the fall of 1932, pasture No. 3 received an application of 3000 pounds of dolomitic limestone per acre. It was an old established sod. In March, 1933, pasture No. 1 received an application of 450 pounds of 16% superphosphate per acre. Pasture No. 2 received no further treatment.

TABLE II

Yields of dry matter per acre per day, and the estimated carrying capacity of 4 plots of grass pasture at Jeanerette, La., in 1931.*

Period of growth	*Plots clipped every 21 days*			
	Plot 3A		*Plot 4A*	
	Dry matter per acre per day	*Area required to support one milking cow*	*Dry matter per acre per day*	*Area required to support one milking cow*
	POUNDS	ACRES	POUNDS	ACRES
Mar. 1 † to May 5	8.3	2.8	7.6	3.1
May 5 to May 26	2.4	9.8	4.0	5.9
May 26 to June 16	.9	26.0	1.9	12.3
June 16 to July 7	.7	33.4	1.0	23.4
July 7 to July 28	4.0	5.9	3.2	7.3
July 28 to Aug. 18	7.4	3.2	8.7	2.7
Aug. 18 to Sept. 8	15.2	1.5	25.7	0.9
Sept. 8 to Sept. 29	5.2	4.5	4.6	5.1

Period of growth	*Plots clipped every 28 days*			
	Plot 3B		*Plot 4B*	
	Dry matter per acre per day	*Area required to support one milking cow*	*Dry matter per acre per day*	*Area required to support one milking cow*
	POUNDS	ACRES	POUNDS	ACRES
Mar. 1 † to May 5	5.5	4.3	6.7	3.5
May 5 to June 2	2.1	11.1	6.2	3.6
June 2 to June 30	1.9	12.3	5.2	4.5
June 30 to July 28	3.2	7.3	2.7	8.7
July 28 to Aug. 25	20.4	1.1	20.1	1.2
Aug. 25 to Sept. 22	16.3	1.4	13.2	1.8

* Table and experimental data supplied by the United States Department of Agriculture (hereafter referred to as U. S. D. A.).

† Growth assumed to start March 1. The last day of each period of growth represents the clipping date.

TABLE III

The rate of stocking and actual average base yield of fat corrected 4% milk by weeks, in grazing tests at the South Carolina Agricultural Experiment Station, 1933.*

Date Week Ending	Pasture No. 1		Pasture No. 2		Pasture No. 3	
	Cows per acre	Lbs. milk per cow-week. Actual average	Cows per acre	Lbs. milk per cow-week. Actual average	Cows per acre	Lbs. milk per cow-week. Actual average
4–12	1.0	359.2	1.0	318.0		
4–19	2.0	334.8	1.0	321.0		
4–26	3.0	305.7	1.5	308.6	1.0	275.9
5–3	3.0	300.4	1.5	304.7	1.0	301.4
5–10	2.0	291.3	1.5	283.6	1.5	258.7
5–17	2.0	276.9	1.5	283.0	2.0	246.5
5–24	1.0	296.2	1.0	260.5	2.0	231.2
5–31	1.0	269.7	1.0	246.4	2.0	240.9
6–7	1.0	284.8	1.0	253.2	1.5	268.1
6–14	1.0	270.5	1.0	236.0	1.5	252.2
6–21	1.0	267.1	1.0	234.3	1.5	241.0
6–28	1.0	257.8	1.0	230.7	1.0	251.1
7–5	1.0	277.2	1.0	244.3	1.0	271.2

Date Week Ending	Pasture No. 1		Pasture No. 2		Pasture No. 3	
	Cows per acre	*Lbs. milk per cow-week. Actual average*	*Cows per acre*	*Lbs. milk per cow-week. Actual average*	*Cows per acre*	*Lbs. milk per cow-week. Actual average*
7–12	1.0	291.4	1.0	244.7	1.0	285.1
7–19	1.5	228.1	1.5	200.7	1.5	246.7
7–26	1.5	217.1	1.5	200.2	1.5	230.3
8–2	1.5	220.7	1.5	202.4	1.5	233.1
8–9	2.0	207.6	1.5	191.4	2.0	255.6
8–16	2.0	201.5	1.5	186.5	2.5	214.6
8–23	2.5	205.5	2.0	196.2	2.5	209.3
8–30	2.5	193.1	2.0	179.8	2.5	196.5
9–6	2.5	182.8	2.0	200.9	2.5	190.4
9–13	2.5	176.1	2.0	191.0	2.5	176.6
9–20	2.5	167.9	2.0	187.0	2.5	194.5
9–27	2.0	178.6	2.0	177.1	2.5	189.2
10–4	2.0	167.8	2.0	168.7	2.5	166.0
10–11	2.0	160.0	2.0	161.5	2.5	149.0
10–18	2.0	164.8	2.0	157.1	2.5	154.2
10–25	2.0	156.2	2.0	147.3	2.5	140.1

* Information and data for table supplied by S. C. Agr. Exp. Sta.

Table III shows the rate at which the three pastures were stocked during the 1933 season, by weekly periods and the average yield per cow of fat corrected 4% milk.

Table IV gives a summary of the total carrying capacity of the three pastures, the total milk produced, the total nutrient requirement, and the net amount of nutrients obtained.

TABLE IV

Summary of pasture returns per acre, season of 1933, in grazing tests at the South Carolina Agricultural Experiment Station.*

	Pasture No. 1	Pasture No. 2	Pasture No. 3
Calendar days continuous grazing	203.0	203.0	189.0
Cow-days (1000 lbs. av. wt.)	368.0	304.5	377.9
Total gain in wt. lbs.	86.5	102.5	110.0
Total 4% milk lbs.	12118.7	9369.6	11055.6
Total digestible nutrient requirement	6971.3	5633.7	6782.9
Total digestible nutrients fed in barn	2349.3	1939.2	2087.9
Total digestible nutrients from pasture	4622.0	3694.5	4695.0
Alfalfa hay equivalent from pasture, tons	4.478	3.580	4.549
Alfalfa hay equivalent per day per cow from pasture, lbs.	24.3	23.5	24.0

* Information and data for table supplied by S. C. Agr. Exp. Sta.

It will be observed that pasture No. 1 showed a yield of 927.5 pounds more of total digestible nutrients per acre than did pasture No 2. The only difference in the treatment of the pastures was the application of 450 pounds of 16% superphosphate per acre on pasture No. 1. The increase on pasture No. 1 attributable to the application of superphosphate was equivalent to 1796 pounds of alfalfa hay, which was obtained for a total cost of $3.55 ($3.15 for superphosphate and 40 cents for labor in applying it). Pasture No. 3 showed a yield of 1000.5 pounds more of total digestible nutrients than did pasture No. 2, or the equivalent of 1938 pounds of alfalfa hay per acre. This was due to a heavy accumulation of manure on this pasture.

Beef cattle grazing experiments in the southeastern states, on the Norfolk series of the coastal plains soils, indicate a possible return of 180 pounds of gain per acre on Bermuda grass, 200 pounds per acre on Bahia grass, 140 pounds per acre on carpet grass, and 220 pounds per acre on centipede grass pastures. These gains were obtained with an application of 320 pounds of 5-9-7 commerical fertilizer per acre in alternating years, and 100 pounds per acre of nitrate of soda for the years when the complete fertilizers were not applied. On sassafras sandy loam on the coastal plain in Maryland, a gain of 234 pounds per acre was obtained as an average for six years' grazing. This soil received an application of lime sufficient to correct acidity and 400 pounds of superphosphate, and 100 pounds of sulphate of potash at the beginning of the experiment.

Pastures on a combination of Tifton sandy loam and Plummers sandy loam along creek bottoms produced 80 pounds of gain per acre with no fertilizer, 280 pounds per acre gain with an application of 600 pounds of 6-12-6 fertilizer, and 260 pounds per acre gain with an application of 600 pounds of 6-12-0 fertilizer per acre.

REFERENCES

Burleson, D. J., *Pastures for Arkansas,* Extension Circular 266, Little Rock, Ark.

Crosby, J. E., Reagan, M. J., and Carter, C. E., *Dairy Pastures,* Circular 271, Mo. Col. of Agr.

Hartwig, H. B., *Seventy-Six Clover Questions Answered,* Bulletin 210, N. Y. State Col. of Agr., Ithaca, N. Y.

Jeffords, S. L., *Better Pastures for South Carolina,* Extension Circular 67, Clemson College, S. C.

Chapter II

FERTILIZATION AND MANAGEMENT

Fertilizing Pastures.—Fertile soil is essential to the profitable production of pasture crops as well as field crops. In too many cases pastures have had a place of secondary importance in the farm program. The wastelands, or those that have been farmed until they are not productive, are turned to pasture. Hillsides that have suffered from washing rains without the protection of terraces are not in a fertile state and cannot be expected to supply an abundance of grazing. The pasture is just as important in the production of feeds for livestock as cultivated lands, and requires just as much fertility for profitable returns. Fields that are worn out from continuous cultivation, or from erosion, are not suited to pasture until the soil is improved.

Information on the fertilization of pastures in the South is limited. However, there is enough data available to prove the value of commercial fertilizer for pasture crops. Soils that have been cropped until their fertility is gone should have a balanced fertilizer; that is, one which contains all three of the essential plant foods—nitrogen, phosphoric acid, and potash. From one to two hundred pounds of 18% superphosphate to the acre, applied in the early spring, is sufficient on most pasture

Fig. 4. Red-polled Cattle on Productive Pasture, Winston-Sal North Carolina. *Courtesy of United States Departm of Agriculture.*

soils. On abandoned farm lands 100 pounds of a complete fertilizer will be the minimum requirement per acre. Use of a fertilizer containing nitrogen under legumes that are supposed to gather their supply of nitrogen from the air, at first may seem to be a contradictory practice. However, legumes can be greatly benefited in the early stages of their growth by the use of nitrates.

Nitrogen applied at the time of planting stimulates the growth of young legume plants, and aids in developing the plants to the grazing stage much quicker where soil nitrogen is scarce.

Phosphorus is a very valuable element in the feed of livestock. The phosphorus content of grasses and clovers may be increased by the application of phosphate fertilizers to the soil. Legumes are more responsive to phosphate than the grasses. Phosphorus is favorable to the development of nodules on the roots of legumes, and furnishes nourishment for their growth.

The Central Experiment Farm at Ottawa, Canada, reports that fertilizers almost doubled the carrying capacity of permanent pastures at Fredericton, New Brunswick. Pasture land not fertilized carried an average of 1.4 cows per acre. Similar land fertilized carried an average of 2.15 cows per acre at Nappan, Nova Scotia. Sheep and lambs made nearly 50% greater gains on fertilized pasture land than on unfertilized at Ottawa.

At the South Carolina Agricultural Experiment Station, during the growing seasons of 1929 and 1932, forty-six plots of old established Bermuda grass pasture were clipped to determine the effect of fertilizers on the yield and composition of the grass. They were clipped at two-week intervals throughout the growing season, and samples taken for chemical analysis.

TABLE V

Summary of results of a coöperative pasture experiment on the effects of fertilizers, and light versus heavy grazing on pastures as indicated by gains in the weights of beef cattle at Jeanerette, La.*

Pasture No.	*Total gains per lot*	*Total cow-days per lot*	*Average gain per animal per day*	*Fertilizer costs per lot*	*Feed costs per lot*	*Total costs per lot*	*Gross † returns per lot*	*Net returns per lot*	*Net returns per acre*
	POUNDS	DAYS	POUNDS	DOLLARS	DOLLARS	DOLLARS	DOLLARS	DOLLARS	DOLLARS
1	1284	1792	.716	Nil	9.08	9.08	77.04	67.96	9.15
2	817	2464	.331	Nil	46.81	46.81	49.02	2.21	.29
3	2119	2260	.937	19.35	7.66	27.01	127.14	100.13	13.29
4	1733	2557	.677	55.91	11.56	67.47	103.98	36.51	4.85

Pasture 1—Received neither lime nor fertilizers and was "light grazed." Its area, 7.42 acres.
Pasture 2—Received neither lime nor fertilizers and was "heavy grazed." Its area, 7.54 acres.
Pasture 3—Received 2.13 tons of ground oyster shell per acre in the fall of 1929, and was treated with annual applications of superphosphate (16%) before the beginning of each pasture season at the rate of 150 pounds per acre. The area of this pasture, 7.53 acres.
Pasture 4—Received 2.2 tons ground oyster shell per acre in the fall of 1929. Superphosphate (16%) was applied before the opening of each pasture season at the rate of 150 pounds per acre. Treatments of sodium nitrate were made each year at the rate of 200 pounds per acre in two equal applications. In 1931 the amount per application was 700 pounds, or a little less than 100 lbs. per acre. The area of this field, 7.52 acres.

Clearing the Land of Bushes, in Preparation for Pasture Crops, Laurens County, Georgia. *Courtesy of Extension Service, United States Department of Agriculture.* Fig. 5.

These tests showed that the application of superphosphate alone caused an increase of 41% in the yield as compared with the yield from the untreated plots. Lime alone increased the yield 33.6%, while lime and superphosphate brought about an increase of 79.5% over the untreated, 34.3% over the lime alone and 27.2% over the superphosphate alone. Fifteen different fertilizer combinations were used in these experiments, and all applications were made at the rate of 600 pounds per acre. The limed series were treated with two tons per acre of ground dolomitic limestone. The soil was Cecil sandy clay loam.

Pasture Management.—Pastures need close attention to get the best returns. It is poor economy to spend money for seed and labor to establish a pasture and leave the crops to take care of themselves. Pasture crops as well as field crops respond to good treatment. Weeds are the worst enemies of pastures. All bushes and underbrush should be cleared away so pasture crops will not be robbed of sunlight and moisture.

Drainage is essential for most pasture plants. While there are a few grasses and legumes that will thrive under excessive moisture, these same crops do well with proper drainage, and livestock are slow to enter wet or boggy areas if other grazing is available. Drainage ditches are necessary to carry the water off the pasture without erosion after heavy rains.

Bermuda and carpet grass sods are improved by breaking or disking lightly during the late winter or early spring, every four or five years. The surface should not be turned. Disking to a depth of an inch or two without turning up the sod is to be preferred, while a harrow or any implement that will scarify the surface will be

Fig. 6. A Hillside Pasture Rendered Unproductive by Erosion.

helpful. Before this operation is started seed of the different crops should be sown where needed on the pasture, and fertilizers applied if necessary.

Grazing Pastures.—Most turf forming grasses thrive under close grazing, that is, a grazing practice that will keep the crops uniformly grazed at all times, allowing a dense turf to form. Care should be used, however, to prevent overgrazing and injury to the stand. What would be close grazing in one locality might be decidedly different in another, depending on the kinds of plants being grazed and the climatic conditions. No set rule could be given that would be safe to follow under all circumstances. Each individual pasture should be managed so as to keep it grazed to capacity at all times. Just what the carrying capacity will be can be determined only by close observation.

The protein content of grass in the early stages of growth is greater than it is in advanced stages. Uniform grazing of pasture crops, on this account, actually gives an increased return from the land.

Testing Soils for Phosphorus.—Recent developments in the field of science make it possible for every farmer or agricultural worker to make a simple test of soils to determine the supply of readily available phosphorus. The trouble and expense of such a test is small and although it is not intended to take the place of a laboratory analysis, it will serve a good purpose in pasture work, and enable one to know whether or not the soil is deficient in available phosphorus. Many failures with pasture legumes are due to phosphorus deficiency, and before much trouble and expense are incurred it is well to know whether or not the soil is in condition to insure success with the legumes. The test consists of taking a measured quantity of soil and mixing with reagents, usually after an extracting solution has been added and the soil filtered, and then reading the color of the mixture against a chart supplied with the equipment. These test kits can be purchased from dealers in scientific equipment.

Phosphorus is one of the most important of the elements required for plant growth. Soils deficient in this element give poor returns. The supply of phosphorus in the soil may be removed by continuous cropping without returning it in the form of fertilizers. The soil is the source of phosphorus for animals through the plants they eat. It is essential for both animal and plant life, and is an

A Dairy Herd on Well-Kept Pasture in Maryland. Fig. 7.
Courtesy of Extension Service, United States Department of Agriculture.

essential constituent in the production of all living cells.

Continuous grazing removes phosphorus from the soil. The bones of animals are chiefly calcium phosphate. Milk is rich in phosphorus. Grazing pasture lands and selling the livestock or livestock products deplete the soil in the course of time by robbing it of phosphorus.

Phosphorus is often present in the soil in a form that is not readily available for plants. This is true in acid soils. Plants dependent upon this form of phosphorus make a slow growth, and maximum yields cannot be expected under such conditions. Liming acid soils will aid in converting the phosphate into a more readily available form where the above mentioned conditions exist.

Supplemental Pastures.—Permanent pastures suffer during extremes of weather. During the dry periods of summer the carrying capacity of sodded areas is greatly reduced. This is also true during the coldest periods of winter. The common summer growing grasses and legumes are not adapted to winter weather conditions.

Good pasture management requires that grazing crops of some kind be supplied throughout the year as nearly as possible. Supplemental pastures in addition to supplying more grazing per acre will provide pasturage at a time when the grazing on permanent pasture areas is at its lowest.

The supplemental pasture program also enables one to produce succulent feeds in greater abundance. They are the means of giving the permanent grazing lands a period of rest, allowing them to recover from heavy grazing. It is a difficult problem to adjust the number of livestock to a pasture area without having the pasture overstocked at certain periods. The supplemental pasture will enable one to solve this problem of grazing, utilizing

'attle Grazing on Temporary Pasture, After Oats, ,aurens County, Georgia. *Courtesy of Extension Serv-:e, United States Department of Agriculture.* Fig. 8.

the supplemental plantings at such times as the other pasture is not able to take care of the animals being grazed upon it.

Supplemental pastures serve a greater purpose to dairymen and those who are growing small herds of animals than would be the case with the larger cattlemen.

Supplemental pastures, because of the type of crops grown upon them, supply from two to four times more green forage to the acre than permanent pasture areas. In grazing experiments at the North Louisiana Experiment Station, it was shown that Sudan grass gave a return of 13.6% more milk per cow daily than did Bermuda grass pasture. The following table shows the results of these experiments with temporary crops.

TABLE VI

Grazing results of temporary crops at North Louisiana Agricultural Experiment Station.*

Av. 4 winters	*Days grazing*	*Milk per day*	*Milk per acre*	*Returns per acre Butterfat $.30 lb.*
Oats and vetch	33	214.7 lbs.	1523 lbs.	$12.56
Rye and vetch	28	211.6 "	1125 "	8.91
Barley and vetch	22	216.0 "	1047 "	7.15
Permanent pasture	48	197.2 "		
Av. 3 summer trials. Sudan	65		1752 "	18.16

* Information supplied by R. H. Lush, La. Agr. Exp. Sta.

In selecting crops for supplemental or temporary pastures it is best to have a mixture of legumes and grasses or small grains. Over the entire South vetches and small grains are excellent winter and spring grazing plants. Italian Rye grass, rescue grass, crimson clover and the sweet clovers are others that may be adapted to supplemental winter grazing. The bur clovers are frequently used, and alfalfa can also be utilized in this way.

Sudan is the most useful plant for summer grazing. Sudan is adapted to practically all southern conditions. A mistake often made in planting Sudan grass is to select the poorer soils. In the production of forage for temporary grazing areas, only the best land should be selected. Sudan will well repay one when planted on good soil.

In the utilization of temporary pastures, care should be used not to overgraze the areas. Sudan grass will produce more forage as a soiling crop because grazing somewhat interferes with the root growth of the plant.

Winter grazing crops are frequently injured in the milder periods of the winter from trampling. This is especially true during periods when the soil is soft and boggy. This trouble can be overcome to some extent by planting the crops on beds four feet wide. The cattle prefer to walk in the solid middles, saving the crops from injury.

Planting information regarding the various grasses and clovers adapted to supplemental grazing will be found elsewhere in this book.

REFERENCES

Aldous, A. E., and Zahnley, J. W., *Tame Pastures in Kansas*, Bulletin 253, Agr. Exp. Sta., Manhattan, Kan.

Lowery, J. C., and Burns, F. W., *Pasture Suggestions*, Extension Circular 110, Auburn, Ala.

Odland, T. E., Garber, R. J., and Dodd, D. R., *Pasture Improvement,* Circular 47, Agr. Exp. Sta., Morgantown, W. Va.

Orr, J. B., and Crichton, A., *Improvement of Permanent Pasture.* Reprint from the *Scottish Journal of Agriculture,* Rowett Research Institute, Aberdeen, Scotland.

Tabor, Paul, and Alexander, E. D., *Pastures for Georgia,* Extension Bulletin 389, Athens, Ga.

Wasson, R. A., *Pasture and Forage Crops for Louisiana,* Extension Circular 140, Baton Rouge, La.

Chapter III

UTILIZATION OF PASTURES

Pasture land of the South is divided into two general classes: (1) That which has never been cultivated, and has developed a growth of natural vegetation; and (2) land previously cultivated and now being utilized for grazing livestock. Much of the land in the first class is unproductive, because of the broken areas and the continued grazing of the lands which in the course of a few years removes considerable fertility.

Lands cultivated for years and then turned back into pastures are usually in a low state of fertility, and are not capable of producing an abundance of nutritious forage. It would not be reasonable to suppose that these abandoned areas would be capable of producing high yields of pasture crops. Until some attention is given to improving conditions on these areas, the grazing results will continue to be unsatisfactory.

Under heavy grazing, pasture land declines in fertility and becomes infested with weeds, animal parasites, and disease-causing organisms. Under proper management, much can be done to eliminate these troubles and to bring the grazing areas into profitable production.

Good pastures not only provide an excellent feed, but they reduce the labor and expense in livestock production by supplying the essential minerals and vitamins for

Fig. 9. A Hillside Pasture on Abandoned Farm Land. Profitabl returns on this kind of land cannot be expected.

body development, and by affording proper environment for animals used for breeding purposes.

Grazing Practices.—In the utilization of pastures, it is well to bear in mind that different animals prefer different kinds of grazing plants. It is necessary to determine the kinds of legumes and grasses growing in the pastures, and then to undertake to adapt the right kind of livestock to the pasture area. It will result in a more uniform grazing of the lands and a higher return in animal products.

Too many sheep on pastures having a large percentage of legumes, such as White Dutch clover, may prove detrimental, as sheep frequently graze entirely on the blossoms at the seeding stage of the crops. Sheep graze the plants much closer than other domestic animals and, for this reason, it is well not to overstock the pasture with sheep.

The palatability of crops being grown on pastures is a decided factor in pasture management. The stage of maturity at which the plants are grazed, as well as climatic and soil conditions, have a bearing on the returns from the lands. Experimental data are at hand to show the superiority of plants grazed in an immature state over those allowed to reach maturity. The tender growth shows a much higher protein content, and is more readily digestible.

"The tender growth of grasses is generally twice as rich in phosphates as the mature grass. The dry matter of immature grass contains approximately four times as much mineral as the average cereal grain, and as much as the average legume hay."[1] The following table gives experimental data on this subject.

[1] A. T. Semple, *A Pasture Handbook,* Miscellaneous Publication 194, U. S. D. A.

TABLE VII

Percentages of the different food elements in immature grass, calculated 10% water content, and of some common dry feeds.*

Feed	*Water*	*Ash*	*Crude protein* (Nx 6.25)	*Crude fiber*	*Starch and sugar* (*nitrogen-free extract*)
Pasturage:					
Bluegrass	10.0	8.0	15.9	23.1	39.1
Pasture mixture	10.0	10.2	16.1	16.9	44.0
Sudan grass	10.0	12.1	12.1	23.4	40.4
Sweet vernal	10.0	5.5	9.7	28.1	44.5
White clover	10.0	12.2	23.4	13.3	38.1
Cereals and cereal products:					
Corn (shelled)	12.9	1.3	9.3	1.9	70.2
Corn (corn-and-cob meal)	15.6	1.5	8.3	6.8	64.4
Oats	7.7	3.5	12.5	11.2	60.7
Wheat bran	9.6	5.9	16.2	8.5	55.6
Wheat middlings or shorts	10.1	3.5	16.3	4.3	61.6
Grass hays:					
Johnson grass	9.0	7.0	8.2	29.7	43.4
Sudan grass	5.3	8.1	9.7	27.9	47.3
Timothy	12.5	5.4	6.8	28.3	44.3
Legume hays:					
Alfalfa	8.3	8.9	16.0	27.1	37.1
Lespedeza	7.9	6.2	11.9	28.5	42.7
Red clover	12.9	6.9	13.6	24.1	39.1
Oil-mill products:					
Cottonseed meal (choice)	7.1	5.7	41.7	10.0	28.4
Linseed meal (old process)	8.9	5.4	34.5	7.7	36.7
Stover and straws:					
Corn stover	10.7	6.1	5.7	30.3	45.7
Oat straw	9.2	5.1	4.0	37.0	42.4
Wheat straw	9.6	4.2	3.4	38.1	43.4

* Courtesy U. S. D. A. From A. T. Semple, H. N. Vinall, C. W. Enlow and Woodward, *A Pasture Handbook,* Miscellaneous Publication 194, U. S. D. A.

Pasture Overstocked with Sheep. The legumes have irely disappeared, giving way to less desirable pasture nts.

Fig. 10.

Where possible to do so, the practice of rotation grazing is an advantage. This would consist of grazing two or more pastures at regular intervals, giving a period of rest to one or more of the pastures at a time, and allowing the crops to develop to the proper stage. Such a system, however, requires close attention to the number of animal units used in order that the areas may be utilized to the best advantage. The carrying capacity of pastures handled in this manner can be materially increased. Rotation grazing, however, is not justified unless close attention can be given to the area being used.

Terracing Pasture Lands.—Terracing or contouring pasture lands will greatly improve conditions for the development of the pasture plants, conserve the soil moisture, and prevent erosion of hillside areas.

Pasture plants require a uniform moisture supply. Decaying vegetable matter in the soil aids in holding the moisture supply, and affords suitable conditions for the bacterial development on the roots of legumes. Hillside pastures, if they are not protected from erosion, will lose a large part of the decaying vegetable matter, especially where the rainfall is heavy. In terracing pasture lands, the terraces should be so constructed that the mower will pass readily over them; otherwise, they will become obstructions on the land and will lessen the possibilities for successful weed control.

Poor hillsides will not show a profitable yield unless the run-off water is handled in such a manner as to prevent the washing away of the humus, rotted vegetation and manure that accumulate on the pasture. Hillsides are much more difficult to seed to pasture crops where they are not terraced, because the light seeds have a tendency to float off with the surface water. Commercial fertilizers applied to unterraced hillsides will not be retained. They will give much better results on the terraced areas.

It is a difficult task to maintain stands of lespedeza on slopes that are not terraced, because the seeds are light and are carried away with the drainage water to the lower area.

Very little experimental data are available on the value of terraces for pasture lands, but it is evident that as much benefit may be expected for pasture crops, as a result of terracing, as would be received for field crops.

The conservation of the moisture supply of hillsides is a very important factor in the production of grazing plants. Pastures are usually at their lowest and most unproductive state during extremely dry periods. Terraces, or contours, will assist in catching and holding the rainfall, insuring that the pastures will survive longer periods of dry weather, and that the soil can be constantly improved with legumes and fertilizers.

Terraces are more important before pastures become sodded than afterward. Once the land becomes sodded there will be very little, if any, erosion on the terraced lands, and the cost of upkeep of the terraces will be practically nothing.

In constructing terraces for pasture lands, the same rule should be followed as for terracing cultivated areas. Ordinarily, on the average pasture, the terrace can be run on a level, but not more than two inches fall per one hundred feet should be given in any case.

Poisonous Plants.—As a rule most plants that are injurious to livestock are unpalatable and not readily taken unless other vegetation is scarce upon the land. However, there are many poisonous weeds in southern pastures that might become harmful under conditions favorable for

Fig. 11. A Hillside Pasture Protected from Erosion by a Syst
of Terraces.

heir development. For this reason, it is well to give special attention to the control of all kinds of weeds in the
pasture. Overgrazing of pastures should be avoided, as
his gives rise to the development of more weeds, and
orces the animals to eat the unpalatable plants that might
be injurious.

Mineral Deficiencies of Pasturage.—In parts of the
Coastal Plain section of Texas, cattle develop a condition
known as loin disease. The animals apparently contract
he disease by chewing bones of animals that die with the
nfection. It is the animal's craving for minerals that leads
t to chew the bones in an effort to supply its own deficiency of phosphorus.

Bone chewing can be prevented by supplying the ani-
nals with sterilized bone meal. This should be kept before
he animals for a large part of the season. A mixture of
one part salt and two parts bone meal is a desirable way
o supply the material. The amount of salt can be increased, if necessary, to hold down the consumption of
he bone meal, bearing in mind that the average salt requirement for mature cattle is about two pounds per
month.

Cattle grazed on certain soils in Florida develop a
nutritional disease known as "salt sick." This condition
s corrected by the addition of iron and a trace of copper
o the supplemental feeds. However, the use of copper
n rations of livestock should be attempted only upon the
advice of a competent veterinarian.

Pasture crops will be deficient in whatever mineral elements are lacking in the soil, and if there is a suspicion
hat the plants are low in the necessary mineral elements,
t is advisable to have a chemical analysis made of the
plants to determine whether or not this is true. If this is

found to be the case, lime and phosphate fertilizers can be applied to the pasture soil, or the minerals can be furnished in the supplemental feeding of the livestock. Phosphorus is essential to the production of healthy legume crops. If these crops fail to produce on the soil it may be an indication of phosphorus deficiency.

Animal Diseases in Relation to Pasture Management.—Water contamination from unsanitary practices has resulted in many outbreaks of animal diseases and infection with internal parasites. Many of the common diseases of livestock are traceable to a bad water supply which has become contaminated by diseased animals, and the failure to dispose of dead animals by burning. Food and water are the source of as much as 90% of all the diseases of the lower animals. It is, therefore, very essential to see that the grazing lands are protected from infection. This can be done by draining stagnant pools, by providing pure drinking water, and by properly disposing of all animals that die on the pasture lands. Carcasses and bones should be completely destroyed, as they may become sources of infection.

Anthrax, hog cholera, hemorrhagic septicemia and tuberculosis are examples of diseases which can be transmitted through the drinking water to cattle and other domestic animals. Internal parasites, such as tape worms, are easily spread through the drinking water, and internal parasites are also frequently carried to the pasture in fresh manure. Manure should be allowed to heat, or to rot thoroughly before being carried to grazing areas.

The Hohenheim System of Grazing.—The Hohenheim system was developed in Germany during the World War in an effort to eliminate the necessity of feeding concentrate rations, which were difficult to obtain at that time.

It was used in the production of milk and dairy products, and the purpose in mind was to make it possible for the animals to obtain all their feed from the pasture.

The original Hohenheim plan called for four applications of nitrogen during the year, one-half to go on in February, and the remainder in the summer.

In operating the plan it is necessary to divide the pasture into several grazing areas of equal size. The following example could be followed. A pasture of say twelve acres can be divided into six two-acre paddocks. Paddock 1 should receive 100 pounds of nitrogenous fertilizer to the acre, with the same application to each succeeding paddock about every five days until all have been fertilized. Grazing should be started on paddock 1 as soon as the pasture crops have made sufficient growth, using from fifteen to twenty high producing cows. The cows should remain on the lot for five or six days, or until they have consumed the best of the pasturage, and then be moved to paddock 2.

After these cows are moved to paddock 2, ten or twelve dairy cattle can be placed on paddock 1 to clean up the remaining pasturage there. The same change should then be made from paddock 2 to 3 and from paddock 1 to 2. The changes can be made at approximately five-day intervals until all six paddocks have been grazed. It is necessary to vary the number of animals used and the length of the grazing period on each paddock, depending upon the size of the paddocks, the number of animals used, and the condition of the pasture. Two or three days after all animals have been removed from a paddock a harrow should be run over the land to scatter the droppings, and another application of fertilizer added to stimulate new growth.

This system of grazing is justified only where the soi is productive and the moisture conditions uniform. Onl the highest producing cattle should be used first, followe by low producers, those out of production, or the youn stock.

Improved Herds in Pasture Utilization.—Pasture im provement and herd improvement go hand in hand. Goo individuals, whether dairy or beef cattle, will respond t a greater degree than if they are scrubs or inferior grades The higher the production of the individual, the greate will be the returns from the better pasture. Animals o equal producing capacity would do equally as well on th same pasture regardless of whether they are pure-bre or grade. The same would probably be true between high grade and poor-bred beef animals. It is true, however that there is a difference in the way in which animals wil utilize their food in the production of milk or beef wit dry feed; and the same difference will undoubtedly pre vail if the animals are on pasture. On the other hand, i is clear that cattle on poor pasture constantly over period of several generations do not have an opportunit to develop to their full capacity; consequently, the bes selection is not possible, and this tends to run the qualit down.

In experimental work at the Georgia Experiment Sta- tion in 1932, it was shown in preliminary reports tha there was a "difference in value as feeders of $5.76 pe head in favor of the higher quality steers when figure on the basis of 400 pounds body weight. From this," th report points out, "one would estimate that if a goo herd bull sires twenty high quality calves annually fo a useful lifetime of only three years, his returns woul amount to approximately $345 more than would an in-

ood Beef Cattle on Excellent Pasture, Aiken County, uth Carolina. Good individuals insure greater returns. *urtesy of Extension Service, United States Department Agriculture.*

Fig. 12.

ferior bull which sired the same number of calves of common grade during the same length of time."[2]

It is very evident that good grade animals capable of utilizing the forage produced on the pastures are essential to the highest returns from the grazing lands. Good pasture management requires that every effort be made to utilize the grasses and legumes produced upon the area to the best advantage.

REFERENCES

Abbott, J. B., and Associates, *Pasture Top Dressing with Fertilizer and Lime;* also, *A Guide to Pasture Management and Fertilization,* published by National Fertilizer Association, Washington, D. C.

Elliott, Walter, *Investigation on the Mineral Content of Pasture Grass.* Reprint from the *Journal of Agricultural Science,* Rowett Research Institute, Aberdeen, Scotland.

Hanley, J. A., and Associates, *Improvement of Pastures.* Reprinted from the *Journal of the Ministry of Agriculture,* Rowett Research Institute, Aberdeen, Scotland.

Orr, J. B., *The Relation of Chemical Composition of Pasture to Its Feeding Value,* Rowett Research Institute, Aberdeen, Scotland.

Orr, J. B., and Allan, H. H., *Restoring the Fertility of Scottish Sheep Grazings,* Rowett Research Institute, Aberdeen, Scotland.

[2] F. R. Edwards, Ga. Exp. Sta., Preliminary Report for 1932.

Chapter IV

THE CONTROL OF WEEDS

Weeds cause an annual loss to farmers in the South of more than a billion dollars. Weeds, in one way or another, cause a loss to the agriculture and industry of the nation amounting to more than two billion dollars a year. It may be said without fear of contradiction that the weed tax in the South is one of the greatest drains upon the farm industry that the farmer has to contend with.

Weeds present one of the most serious problems in pasture development. They rob the soil of moisture and plant food, and thus retard the growth of pasture plants. Many species are poison to livestock, and may endanger the life of animals that eat them. They harbor insects and diseases that may become destructive to cultivated crops, reduce the amount of grazing, and add to the cost of pasture upkeep. Grasses and clovers require plenty of moisture and sunshine as well as plant food. Most pasture soils are low in plant foods and, when this must be divided with a crop of weeds and the remainder used by the pasture plants along with a lack of moisture and sunlight, the plants will gradually give way to the weeds and the value of the pasture will decrease from year to year.

Weeds Harbor Insect Pests and Plant Diseases.—If weeds could be eradicated completely, many of our plant diseases could be controlled. Many species of weeds serve as hosts for diseases common to field and vegetable crops. The organisms causing cotton root-rot live on certain weeds. Some of the wild legumes have bean blight. Certain species of wild mustard are subject to attacks from the fungus that causes club root in cabbage, and the organisms that are responsible for blackleg of cabbage. The beet-leaf hopper lives in weeds. The cotton-leaf hopper breeds on the common goat weed, or croton. Grasshoppers live in weeds where protection enables them to deposit great numbers of eggs which later hatch and cause losses to pasture and field crops in the spring. Many common pasture weeds serve as hosts to insects or diseases of some kind, and weed control measures directed at pasture improvement will aid in the control of both insects and plant diseases.

How Weeds Spread.—The seeds of most weeds will keep their vitality in the soil for many years. Experiments on the germination of weed seeds have shown that some of them may remain buried in the soil for thirty years and germinate when brought near the surface where conditions are favorable for germination. The seeds of purslane, shepherd's purse, dock, pigweed and some others are known to live for more than thirty years. Seed of mallow survive in the soil for five or ten years, and many others keep their vitality for four or five years.

Most weeds bear seed freely, some of them producing an almost unbelievable number. For example, purslane produces normally about 1,250,000 seeds per plant; pigweed, about 1,000,000 per plant; and dock, about 500,000

Fig. 13. Alfalfa Seed Adulterated with Dodder. *Courtesy of Extension Service, United States Department of Agriculture.*

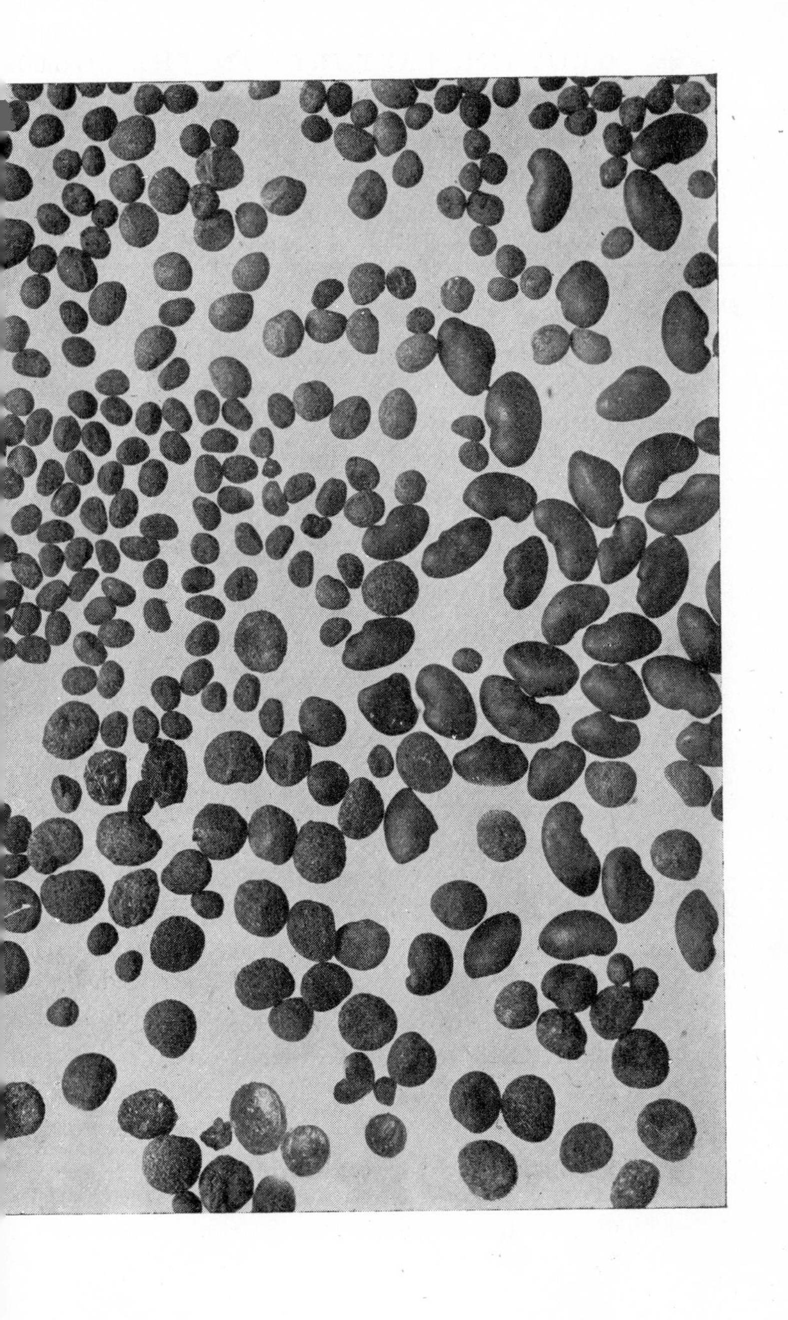

per plant. When it is remembered that seeds of some weeds keep their vitality in the soil for at least thirty years this, combined with their seeding habits, presents a problem in weed control worthy of serious thought and careful planning.

Farmers should be on intimate terms with the worst weed pests of their pastures and cultivated lands. Not only should they be able to recognize the weeds by name, but they should also be able to know them by their seeds and to detect weed seeds among seeds of cultivated crops at the time of purchase. The introduction of serious weed pests with pasture crops is likely to occur if the pasture crops to be planted are not known to be free of noxious weed seeds.

Weeds multiply much faster than clovers and cultivated grasses. Clovers that normally produce as many as one thousand seeds per plant, under heavy grazing may not return to the soil more than twenty to forty seeds per plant; while weeds, as already pointed out, may return as many as 1,000,000 or more seeds per plant. Weeds are not grazed as readily as pasture plants and, when once started, weeds may soon completely take a pasture and crowd out the useful pasture crops.

Methods of Weed Control—Successful weed control in pastures requires some knowledge of the species and their habits of growth.

Annual weeds are those that live but one year. The biennials live two years. Both bear a crop of seed and die down, root and all. There are no underground parts of an annual or biennial weed by which it may spread. It depends solely upon its seed crop for its spread. This being true, the only means necessary to control annuals or biennials is to prevent them from going to seed. If this

eep Aid in the Control of Weeds in Pastures. *Courtesy Extension Service, United States Department of Agri- lture.* Fig. 14.

is done for a few seasons, the weeds will disappear unless seed is brought in from other areas.

Perennial weeds are those that live for three years or more and spread both by seed and by underground roots or stems. If seeding can be controlled, the spread of these plants will be confined to the roots and stems that grow underground. The top growth is essential to the development of the underground parts, so a consistent program of mowing to prevent top development is the most satisfactory means of control. Mowing in early spring and forcing the plant to use up the reserve supply of plant food in the roots is a good practice in perennial weed control. It is generally true that the mower is the worst enemy of weeds, whether annuals, biennials or perennials.

Grazing and Weed Control.—Weeds multiply and spread fastest on undergrazed pastures. Where a sufficient number of livestock are kept on a pasture to keep the grass properly grazed, the young weeds will be destroyed in their early growth. Where possible, the pasture should be grazed to full capacity at all times.

Sheep are very effective in the control of weeds in pastures. Where sheep have the run of pastures, they are usually almost free of weeds.

Overgrazing must be avoided. When pasture crops are overgrazed, weeds usually take advantage of the opportunity to establish themselves. Good pasture management requires that the right number of livestock be kept on the grazing areas at all times. If pasture crops show a tendency to disappear and give way to weeds, it will usually be necessary to fertilize the pasture. Anything that will encourage a uniform and vigorous growth of pasture plants will hold the weeds in check.

Bitterweed.—The bitterweed (*Helenium tenuifolium*) is one of the worst pests of Southern pastures. It is most abundant from Virginia and Missouri to the Gulf Coast, but is occasionally found farther north. The bitterweed causes the heaviest losses to dairymen by causing bitter unmarketable milk. The Bureau of Dairy Industry of the United States Department of Agriculture has made a care-ul study of the effect of bit-erweed on milk and milk products. They have found hat bitterweed is present in nilk produced twenty-four ours after cows have con-umed as much as ten pounds f the weed.

Fig. 15. Common Bitterweed.

The *Yearbook* of the United States Department of Agriculture for 1927 states hat, "Cows must consume ½ to 5 pounds of bitter-eed one hour before milking, or 2½ to 3 pounds (one-alf pound at one-hour intervals) to within two hours f milking before its effect will be noticed. These amounts roduce very slightly bitter milk. As the quantity of bit-erweed consumed increases, the intensity of the bitter avor in the milk also increases. When more than seven ounds are consumed, bitter milk is produced, and more ian nine pounds produces very bitter milk."

Bitterweed control in pastures requires a carefully lanned program of grazing and mowing. Where neces-ary, fertilizers should be applied to stimulate the growth the grasses. A heavy growth of such grasses as carpet and Bermuda will aid materially in keeping bitterweeds under control. As soon as the first flowers appear on the weeds, the pasture should be mowed. The first mowing should clip the weeds six or eight inches above the ground. This will allow the second crop of flowers to appear high enough to be destroyed by the second mowing. A third mowing may be necessary, the purpose being to prevent seeding.

Poison Bitterweed.—A weed pest called poison bitterweed (*Actinea odorata*) has been shown by the Texas Agricultural Experiment Station to be poisonous to sheep. In feeding tests, the station found that in some cases as little as 500 grams of immature green bitterweed, when given over a period of two days, was sufficient to cause the death of the animal. Other animals tolerate much larger amounts. This weed makes its appearance in early fall, and matures in April or May. It grows from Kansas south to Mexico, and from Central Texas to California, being most abundant in the Edwards Plateau region of Texas. Control must consist of preventing seeding, either by establishing a heavy sod of grass to crowd it out, or by mowing.

Wild Garlic.—One of the most troublesome weeds in southern pastures is wild garlic (*Allium vineale*). When it once becomes established in pastures, it is a source of trouble to dairy farmers because of the tainted milk produced by cows eating it.

On pasture lands, wild garlic usually grows in clumps, a habit which makes it more easily controlled. Wild garlic rarely produces seed. The heads are composed of a cluster of bulblets, and the plants usually produce five or six bulbs underground, which may be found at the base of the plants at maturity.

Cultivation, the best method of control, is not practical on pasture lands. Close grazing is the best method of control on pasture lands, the purpose being to prevent he development of the tops. Where wild garlic has a start n pastures as many animals should be allowed the run of the grazing areas as is practical without injury to the pasture crops.

Wild Onion.—Wild onion (*Allium canadense*) also occurs in pastures in the South. It is often mistaken for wild garlic. The wild onion has only a single underground bulb, and its leaves are flattened, whereas wild garlic has hollow, round, or cylindrical leaves, with a cluster of bulbs underground, these latter found between the leaf ayers of the parent bulb. Wild onion will usually disappear under close grazing.

Bracted Plantain.—Bracted Plantain (*Plantago aris-ata*) is a common weed in pastures of the South, growing upon practically all the soil types where pasture crops are growing. It is an annual, making its appearance early in he spring, but because of its resemblance to grass it is not noticed until the bracted spikes appear. Until the bracted spikes appear the plant is not objectionable in pastures. It is very prolific, producing a large number of seeds, and spreads rapidly over pasture areas unless con-rol measures are started as soon as it makes its appearance. There are several other species of Plantain found n southern pastures that may be classed as worthwhile crops for grazing, being more or less nutritious and pala-able to livestock. Among these are narrow leaved plan-ain and broad leaved plantain.

It has been discovered that mowing to prevent the formation of seed spikes is decidedly the best means of control.

Rough Marsh Elder.—(*Iva ciliata.*) This is a common pest in pastures of the Gulf coastal prairies where it frequently grows so dense as to shade the ground and smother out grasses and clovers. It occurs on wastelands and pastures in other parts of the South, and northward to Illinois and Nebraska. It is a coarse bristly weed from two to seven feet high. It produces seed from September to November.

The best means of control of this pest is to mow the pastures before the seed heads mature. It occurs mostly on pastures that are undergrazed.

Poverty Weed.—(*Iva angustifolia.*) This pest is common in pastures throughout the Gulf coastal area, as well as in other parts of the South. It is an annual, and spreads by seeds. It sometimes occurs in cultivated crops and grain fields. It is disliked by animals, which fact accounts for its forming a dense growth, and often crowding out valuable pasture plants. It grows from six inches to two feet high.

Several mowings during the growing season are necessary to prevent the production of seed.

August Weed.—(*Dichrophyllum bicolor.*) Also called white top and "snow on the prairie," this is a weed common in pastures throughout the Gulf coastal area, although it may be found in other parts of the South. These weeds develop on pastures that are undergrazed.

Proper pasture management will go a long way toward control of this pest. It seeds from August to November. Mowing to prevent the formation of seed heads is the most practical means of control.

Ironweed.—There are several species of ironweed, *Vernonia* species, found in southern pastures. These weeds are perennials, and are propagated by seeds which occur

rom July to September. They sometimes occur in culti-
'ated crops.

Inasmuch as these pests do not persist in extremely arge numbers in pastures, it is sometimes desirable to ut the weeds below the urface with a grubbing ioe to prevent them from oing to seed. If the tops ire not allowed to develop, he food in the roots will e exhausted, and the lant will eventually dis-ppear from the pasture. Mowing to prevent seed roduction is a sure means f control.

Fig. 16. Dodder on Alfalfa. *Courtesy of Extension Service, United States Department of Agriculture.*

Dodder. — (*Cuscuta* sp.) These parasitic plants ire common throughout he south. The seed of hese parasites germinate n the soil, but the young lants only remain there ong enough to allow them o develop to a size when hey can attach themselves o the host plant, at which ime they disconnect from the soil entirely and draw their sustenance from the sap of the host plants. The small wart-like suckers enable dodder to be very destructive n clover fields. The yellowish-red threads develop in every direction, forming a dense mass.

The best means of control of this pest is to burn the

areas where it is observed, or spray them thoroughly with kerosene or some reliable weed killer. If the seeds are allowed to mature, the vines and host plants should be cut and burned on the spot where they were produced.

There are several species of dodder, including field dodder (*C. arvensis*) and common dodder (*C. gronovii*). They are often called love vines, strangle weed and devil's hair.

White Snakeroot.—(*Eupatorium urticaefolium.*) This weed is common in woodland pastures in the hilly and mountainous sections of the South. It has been definitely proven to be the cause of milk sickness or trembles in animals and man. Animals poisoned with this plant develop a disease called trembles, and persons eating milk or butter from an animal affected with this poison have a disorder known as milk sickness.

As this weed occurs mostly in open woods, thickets and along streams, control by mowing is not always possible. Grubbing the weeds out by the roots will be the most practical means of control under these conditions. It grows from one to four feet tall, is much branched, and has large compound snowy white flower clusters. It is a perennial, propagated by seeds.

Broom sedge, species of everlasting, sticktight, cocklebures and sandburs are other troublesome pasture pests. These can be controlled, as other weeds, by a consistent program of mowing and grazing.

REFERENCES

A Suggested Program of Weed Control, published by Chamber of Commerce of the United States, Washington, D. C., 1930.

Ball, W. S., Madison, B. A., and Robbins, W. W., *The Control of Weeds,* Circular 54, College of Agriculture, Berkeley, Calif.

Georgia, Ada, *Manual of Weeds,* New York, 1923.

Hardy, W. T., Cory, V. L., Schmidt, H., and Dameron, W. H., *Bitterweed Poisoning in Sheep,* Bulletin 433, Agr. Exp. Sta., College Station, Texas.

Talbot, M. W., *Chemical Weed Killers,* Leaflet of Bureau of Plant Industry, U. S. D. A.

Chapter V

THE GRASS FAMILY

The grass family outranks all other families of the vegetable kingdom in usefulness. Broadly speaking, the grasses are all plants included in the botanical family known as *Poaceae* or *Gramineae,* which includes such species as the bamboos; and the grains such as wheat, corn and rice, as well as the smaller species of meadow and pasture plants commonly used for grazing and hay, and valuable as forage for farm animals.

Grasses are found wherever vegetation of any kind can grow, from the tropics where they are found in great abundance to the far North. Wherever man is found they are utilized in some way, either as sources of food or raiment for man or animals, or as shelter. The human race could not long exist without the grasses.

Classification as to Uses.—Grasses are classified according to their uses into several divisions. The two most important of these divisions are the grain and forage plants. Others of more or less importance are lawn grasses, sugar-producing species such as ribbon cane, textile grasses, soil binders, and the ornamental group. We are primarily concerned with a discussion of the forage plant group.

This book is intended as a practical treatise of pasture

and forage plants with as little reference to technical terms as possible. However, it may be well to refer to the characteristics of the grass family, and at the same time to make a short reference to the structure of grasses, and more especially to the relationship of species.

Latin Names of Plants.—Plants in the great majority of cases are referred to by their common names. The common name of a grass in one locality may be entirely different from the common name in another locality. This makes it necessary to have one name by which the particular plant may be known the world over. Dallis grass might not identify any particular grass to a resident of a foreign country, but *Paspalum dilatatum* would definitely point it out, because it bears this name in botanical works in all languages.

In classifying plants, botanists have attempted to place them according to the degree of relationship. The entire plant kingdom is divided into four great groups—the *Thallophytes,* simple forms without roots, stems or leaves, including the bacteria, algae, fungi and lichens; the *Bryophytes,* or moss plants, including liverworts and mosses; the *Pteridophytes,* or fern plants, including true ferns, horsetail rushes and club mosses; and the *Spermatophytes* or seed plants, including only those that bear seed.

The grass family of the last named group consists of a great variety of forms. Most writers recognize about 400 genera of grasses, made up of more than 4700 species. The grass family *Poaceae* is divided into two series, being distinguished by the structure of the inflorescence. Series 1, the *Panicoideae,* includes six tribes; and series 2, the *Poacoideae,* includes seven.

Classification of Plants.—The great number of different plants and their varying degrees of relationship make it imperative to have some system by which each of them may be identified and their differences defined. Under this system of classification plants are divided into groups, the highest group being the class, then the order, family, genus and species.

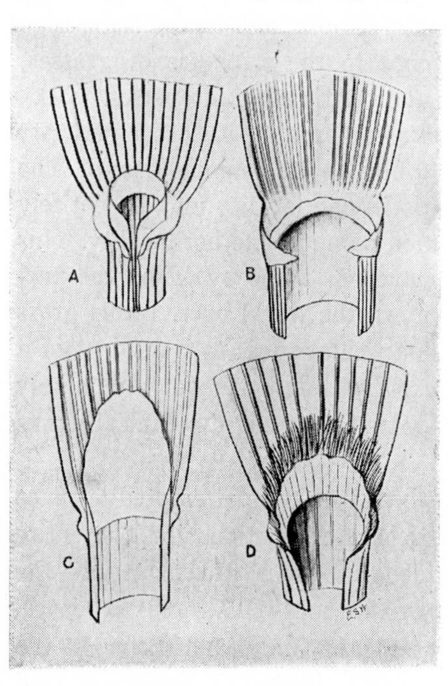

Fig. 17. Structures About the Collar: A. Italian Rye Grass, showing ligule and narrow flangelike auricle; B. Meadow Fescue with very short ligule and sharp-pointed auricles; C. Red Top with somewhat crenulate ligule but no auricles; D. Johnson Grass with fringed ligule. *Courtesy of United States Department of Agriculture.*

Each plant is given a Latin name consisting of two parts. The first word indicates the genus to which it belongs; and the second, the species of the plant. The genus name is what we might term the surname, and the species, the baptismal name. For instance, all Paspalums combine to make up one genus of grasses. Each different kind of Paspalum, although of the same genus, is in itself a species, and bears a species name different from all others. For example, *Paspalum dilatatum* and *Paspalum almum* both belong to the same genus but different species, one being *dilatatum* species and the other *almum*. A species is said to consist of a group of plants closely enough related to make them capable of freely interbreeding. The genus includes all of these species.

Fig. 18. Forms of Inflorescence: (a) panicle; (b) raceme; (c) spike.

Structural Characteristics of Grasses.—All grasses have fibrous roots, and usually hollow stems, although the stems are solid in some species such as corn and sugar cane. The vegetative part of a grass plant consists of the root, stem and leaves. The stems are called culms, and the joints are referred to as nodes. The part of the stem between the joints is the internode. The leaves in grasses are always two-ranked; that is, each leaf grows on the opposite side of the stem from the one below it. In other words, this makes the third leaf come directly above the first, and the fourth directly above the second.

The leaf consists of the sheath and blade. The sheath surrounds the stem like a tube, split down one side. The part of the leaf where the blade and sheath join is called the collar. In some grasses the collar bears a projection called the auricle. In some species the inner side of the collar has a delicate flap called the ligule. At the terminal of the shoot or stem is found the flowers that make up the seed head or inflorescence.

The seed head of a grass, or the inflorescence, may take either one of three forms. It may be an open-branched cluster known as a panicle, a flower cluster

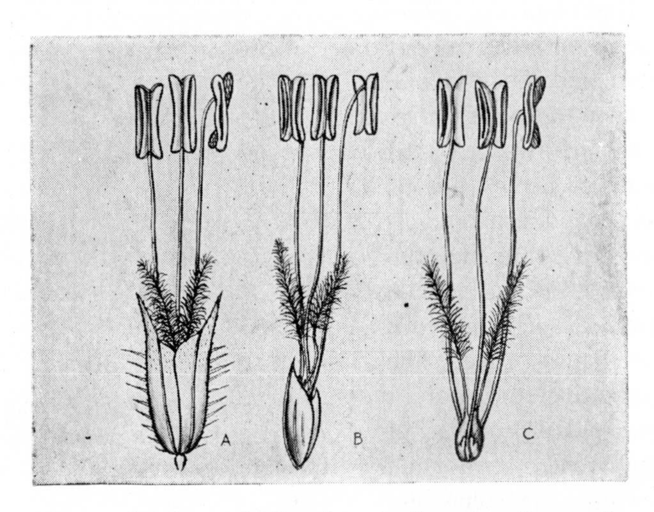

Fig. 19. A Floret of Timothy: A. Complete floret—the two hairy scales are the glumes; B. The glumes removed—the scale on the left is the lemma, that on the right the palea; C. The naked flower, consisting of three stamens and an ovary bearing two feathery stigmas—the two minute scales are lodicules. (Much enlarged) *Courtesy of United States Department of Agriculture.*

arranged along one side of the flower stalk and called a raceme, or it may appear with spikelets set around and snugly against the stem or axis and called a spike.

The flowers, or florets, combine to make up the spikelet, and the spikelet is the unit of inflorescence. The spikelet is made up of the glumes and florets, two ranked and alternate on the axis or rachilla. The floret is made up of one lemma, one palea, and the enclosed flower. The flower consists of the pistil with the ovary and the two feathery stigmas. Three stamens surround the pistil, each stamen with a slender stalk and the pollen-bearing anther.

The roots of grasses are never jointed. In some grasses stems, or parts of stems, are borne on the underground portions of the plant, and may be mistaken for the roots. These jointed underground stems are called rhizomes. The rhizomes are jointed and send up shoots from the joints, forming new plants. In some grasses the stems borne at the base of the plant run on the surface of the ground. When this is the case the runners are called stolons. A grass may have both rhizomes and stolons. Bermuda grass is an example.

REFERENCES

Brown, H. B., and Ricks, J. R., *Grasses and Forage Plants,* Extension Bulletin 3, State College, Miss.

Chase, Mrs. Agnes, *First Book of Grasses,* New York, 1922.

Dayton, W. A., *Glossary of Botanical Terms,* Miscellaneous Publication 110, U. S. D. A.

Hitchcock, A. S., *Manual of the Grasses of the United States,* Miscellaneous Publication 200, U. S. D. A.; also *A Text-book of Grasses,* New York, 1914.

Piper, Chas. V., *Important Cultivated Grasses,* Farmer's Bulletin 1254, U. S. D. A.; *Cultivated Grasses of Secondary Importance,* Farmer's Bulletin 1433, U. S. D. A.

Robinson, B. L., and Fernald, M. L., eds., *Gray's New Manual of Botany,* 7th edition, New York, 1914.

Silveus, W. A., *Texas Grasses,* San Antonio, Texas, 1933.

Chapter VI

THE PASPALUMS

The Paspalums make up a genus of approximately 400 species[1] distributed throughout the southern states, as well as other parts of the Western Hemisphere. They are abundant in South America. A few are of worldwide distribution, and are probably of American origin. They are found growing under many soil and climatic conditions. They are primarily grasses of the tropics and warm temperate regions. Many of them are coarse and unpalatable to livestock. Comparatively few have become of economic importance as pasture and forage crops in the South.

The species that have been found valuable for pastures are fast growing and very nutritious, resisting the hot summer sun remarkably well. Being largely perennials, they afford some grazing during warm winter weather and recover from light frosts and freezes in a very short time. While some of the species common to the lower South such as Dallis and Vasey grass are said to prefer low moist lands, they are found growing under drouthy conditions and will survive without rain for weeks.

Combs' Paspalum.—(*Paspalum almum*, Chase.) This species of Paspalum was discovered by the author growing on the farm of Edwin Rake in Jefferson County,

[1] Chase, Mrs. Agnes, *The North American Species of Pasplaum.*

Fig. 20. Combs' Paspalum.

Texas, in 1929. It was not accepted as a new species, however, until September 1932, when specimens sent to the National Herbarium were identified by Mrs. Agnes Chase, who gave it its common as well as its Latin name.

Combs' Paspalum has been found in a limited area in Jefferson County, Texas, and has been observed by cattlemen for several years in this area. In the section where it is found it is one of the best grasses for grazing, and survives trampling remarkably well.

Combs' Paspalum is adapted to either loams or clays, and thrives under the same conditions required for Dallis and Vasey grass. It quickly recovers from drouth or frost injury when weather conditions are favorable. Any soil that will produce carpet grass will be adapted to Combs' Paspalum. It will make an excellent growth on bottom lands that do not stand under water for any length of time during the season. Its range of usefulness is not well known; however, it will behave as a perennial where the temperature does not drop below 20° F. Its free seeding habits will make it profitable as a grazing crop, since it comes from the seed each spring.

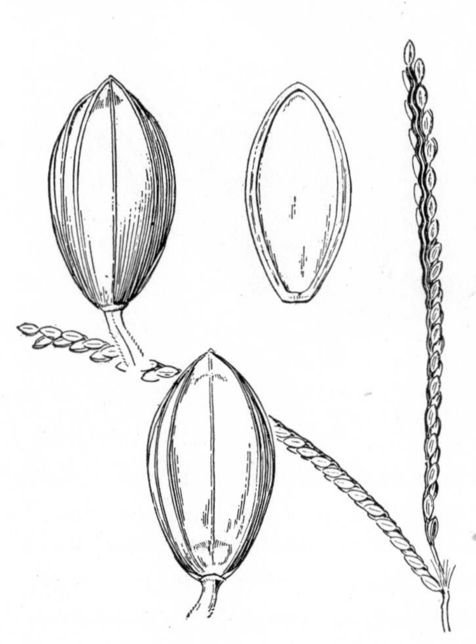

Fig. 21. Seed Head of Combs' Paspalum. *Courtesy of Chase, United States Department of Agriculture.*

It is very palatable and nutritious and livestock show a marked preference for it, hunting it out among other pasture grasses. It seeds freely and the seed show a high percentage of germination. This habit causes it to spread rapidly when once introduced in a pasture, forming a very dense turf or carpet that stands its own remarkably well with weeds and other grasses. The seeds are free of smut or fungous growth, and are produced on small stems from three to twelve inches high. The seed begin to appear early in the season and continue until frost.

The seeds shatter badly and, for this reason, are not

easily harvested. Where the crop is not grazed too closely, the seed stems will grow more erect. Probably the most practical way to harvest seed on the farm is to attach a pan to the mower blade to catch seed that shatter. Successive cuttings in this manner during the season when seed is ripe will result in well-matured seed that will show a high percentage of germination.

It is easily started from plants or portions of plants which live readily and show quick growth. If it is started from plants the bunches may be divided easily, each portion being sufficient for starting a new bunch that will begin seed bearing by May or June. Spring plantings from seed are to be preferred, five pounds of seed to the acre being sufficient where other pasture grasses are to have equal importance in the planting program.

It is more satisfactory in combination with other pasture grasses and with Lespedeza, White Dutch and other clovers, than when planted alone for pasture purposes. It makes a good soil binder due to its heavy root system and dense turf.

Dallis Grass.—(Paspalum dilatatum.) Dallis grass is probably the most popular of the Paspalums for pasture in the lower South, where it occupies an important place in the pasture improvement programs. It has gained its popularity by proving itself adapted to a great variety of soil and climatic conditions.

This grass was introduced into the United States some time before 1879, and was first observed around New Orleans, Louisiana, from which locality it has spread to all parts of the cotton belt. It has spread naturally to most of the range lands in the Gulf Coast, and in that locality affords considerable winter grazing. It is not injured by light freezes, and will remain under water for

Fig. 22. Dallis Grass.

days without injury. Its apparent liking for wet lands first led to the belief that it was a water grass, and it was called "water Paspalum." However, it has been found to be adapted to practically every condition where rainfall is as much as thirty inches a year throughout the Cotton Belt.

Dallis grass grows on a large variety of soils, but prefers heavy soils, or loam. Loose sands in the hilly regions dry out in summer and on these soils it suffers for lack of moisture. Dallis grass will be more satisfactory for a grazing crop on low lands than it will on hillsides, unless the rainfall is plentiful during the summer months.

Dallis grass gives best results in mixtures. Alone it fails

to cover the ground densely enough to form a good sod. It combines well with Bermuda and carpet grasses, and once started in mixture keeps a satisfactory balance with other crops. Heavy grazing does not injure it.

Lespedeza will grow well with Dallis grass mixtures, but with Dallis grass alone the young Lespedeza plants are shaded and crowded out to some extent. White Dutch, alsike, hop and the bur clovers do well in combination with Dallis grass where the soil is adapted to their growth.

A disadvantage of Dallis grass in pastures is the possibility of ergot poisoning of livestock from eating the seed heads infected with a fungus known as *Claviceps paspali*. This disease of the seed heads is evidenced by a black smut in the seed. Although it has been a source of trouble in comparatively few localities, it is well to look out for it and, if animals show any traces of "ergotism," they should be removed from the pasture at once and given a drench of Epsom salts. This simple treatment is usually all that is required to check the poisoning. The possibility of ergot poisoning is so remote that it should not influence anyone against the grass where cattle are kept under close observation. A reddish fungus, *Fusarium graminum*, common on the heads is sometimes mistaken for ergot. Close grazing or mowing to prevent a heavy production of seed stalks will remove almost entirely the dangers from ergot poisoning.

As a rule seed produced by Dallis grass in the South show a poor germination. Most seed for planting are imported from Australia. On soils of limestone origin, Dallis grass eight to twelve pounds; Lespedeza, ten pounds; and White Dutch clover three pounds to the acre, is a mixture that will prove satisfactory. This mixture would be suitable where a reasonably good stand of Bermuda or other grasses are already growing. If there are no other grasses growing on the land, they should be supplied. Black medic, hop clover, Persian clover and Alsike clover are others that may be added to advantage. On acid soils, alsike clover, hop clover and Lespedeza would be best with it. Spring seedings, after danger of frosts, are to be desired, although fall seedings have been found successful in the milder climates of the lower South.

Dallis grass is a native of South America, from Brazil to Argentina. It is found in the United States from New Jersey southward to Florida, and west to Arkansas and Texas. It is also found in California, Arizona, Colorado and Oregon. It has been introduced into the West Indies and other foreign countries. It is known under several different names, including large water grass, hairy-flowered paspalum, and golden crown grass. A. T. Dallis, a Georgia farmer, first made its merits known to the public. It afterward came to be known as Dallis grass. It is a perennial bunch grass with a deep root system, with several slender seed stalks from two to four feet high.

Vasey Grass.—(*Paspalum urvillei.*) Vasey grass is common throughout the lower South, especially along the Gulf Coast. Its upright growth prevents its surviving trampling or grazing as well as some of its relatives, but its value as a hay crop is at once recognized wherever it is grown. Vasey, like many other of the Paspalums, will survive under extremes of soil and climate. It is found growing abundantly in wet land, and upon well-drained soils where moisture is scarce for weeks. It succeeds on both light and heavy soils.

Along the Gulf Coast Vasey grass is common on waste-lands, where it soon crowds out the low growing species It is spreading gradually because of its free seeding

Fig. 23. A Vasey Grass Hay Meadow, Jefferson County, Texas.

habits. On closely grazed pastures Vasey grass gradually disappears. If allowed to grow throughout the season it will often reach a height of from four to six feet, and begins to mature seed as early as June. The ascending stems lose some of their palatability by age and, if the crop is to be cut for hay, it should be cut as soon as the plant is twenty or thirty inches high. A second cutting, or even the third or fourth, depending upon the soil and climate, may be obtained.

Vasey grass makes an excellent quality hay and is worthy of a place on the farm for this purpose. Hammock or bottom lands are best adapted to its growth for this purpose, since a lack of moisture would prevent a large

crop of hay. Being a perennial, it survives the winte
and recovers from freezes in a few days, giving excellen
grazing early in the spring with some grazing durin
warm periods in the winter.

Due to the fact that all the seed crop is never matur
at any time during the summer, it is believed best t
attempt seed harvesting in the fall. By September ther
is usually a heavy crop of mature heads. The seeds shat
ter badly when ripe, and for this reason it is difficult t
harvest the seeds that are fully mature. The seeds tha
remain on the heads when the grass is cut are usuall
immature, and will show a poor germination. The fal
cutting affords the best opportunity for harvesting an
saving mature seed. If planted for a hay meadow, thirt
pounds of seed to the acre should be used broadcast an
the soil disked lightly after the seeds are sown. Planting
should be made about the usual corn planting time. O
sod lands the seed may be sown in the fall to come up i
the spring. This will allow plenty of time for the ligh
seed to settle through the turf and reach the soil b
spring, nature's way of spreading it. The flowering culm
or stems are from four to six feet high.

Vasey grass is a close relative of Dallis grass. It is
native of South America, and was introduced into th
United States some time before 1880. It is found fron
"North Carolina to Florida and west to Texas; also i
Southern California, Guatemala and Cuba; native fron
Brazil to Argentina; introduced in Bolivia, Chili, an
the Hawaiian Islands."[2] It is an erect perennial bunc
grass with seed stalks three to six feet high. Each flowe
cluster bears from ten to twenty-five spikes, more com
monly ten to eighteen.

[2] Mrs. Agnes Chase, *The North American Species of Paspalum.*

airy Cattle on Bahia Grass Pasture in Florida. *Courtesy* Fig. 24.
Florida Experiment Station.

Bahia Grass.—(*Paspalum notatum.*) Bahia grass has become popular in recent years as a pasture grass in Florida. It has been most successful on the light Norfolk sands. It supplies grazing throughout the spring, and does not become coarse or unpalatable with age.

Bahia grass makes such a compact sod on adapted soils that legumes are very likely to be crowded out when planted in mixtures with it. Like Dallis grass, the seed heads of Bahia grass are subject to attack of a fungus that causes trouble to cattle that graze upon it in this stage. Injury to cattle from this source is common in South America where it grows abundantly, but injury from this cause is rare in the South. Close grazing or mowing to prevent the formation of a heavy crop of seed heads will remove practically all danger from this source.

Most seed of Bahia grass for planting is obtained from Cuba. For some reason the seed show a very low germination. This is due, to some extent at least, to the fact that fully mature seed shatter easily making it difficult to harvest them. Where seed are allowed to mature on the plants and are scattered in the natural way, the grass spreads rapidly, and the seed germination is more satisfactory. Bahia grass is easily propagated by division and can be successfully introduced into pastures in this manner. Spring plantings on a firm seed bed are most successful. In mixture with other crops, from ten to twenty pounds of seed to the acre are required for best results.

Bahia gross is a perennial, similar in appearance to carpet grass. The seed stems are usually about one foot high with a two branched panicle. This grass forms a dense turf and is readily grazed. It is used extensively for pastures in Cuba and Puerto Rico, and is common in Uruguay, Brazil and Argentina. It was introduced into the southern United States, and has become popular wherever grown, but has been most popular in Florida. It produces seed abundantly throughout the warm season.

Paspalums of Secondary Importance

Paspalum vaginatum.—This plant is found along the seacoast from North Carolina to Florida, and in the Gulf Coast where it has become established to a small extent

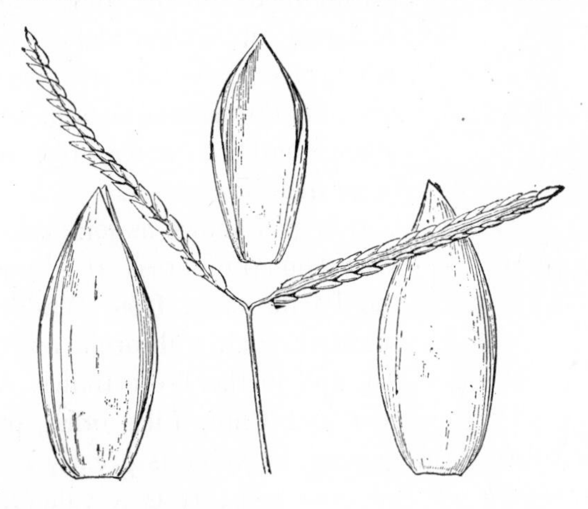

Fig. 25. A Seed Head of *Paspalum vaginatum.* *Courtesy of Chase, United States Department of Agriculture.*

as a grazing crop. It is worthy of further trial, and has been found adapted to the brackish sands and lowlands of the lower South. *P. vaginatum* is a perennial with creeping habits, and will persist under grazing.

Like many other of the Paspalums, *P. vaginatum* is adapted to a rather wide range of soil and climatic conditions, being found in Mexico, West Indies, Argentina and Chili, as well as subtropical coasts of the Old World.

It can be profitably introduced in many pasture areas in the lower South.

Knotgrass.—(*Paspalum distichum.*) This is a widely creeping perennial found in scattered areas from New Jersey to Florida and west to Tennessee and Arkansas. It furnishes excellent grazing in the lowlands near the coast, but where it occurs in the cotton fields of the Black Belt of Alabama, it is considered a pest. Knotgrass grows on rich, wet and dry soils throughout Georgia and the other southern states, but not in large quantities.

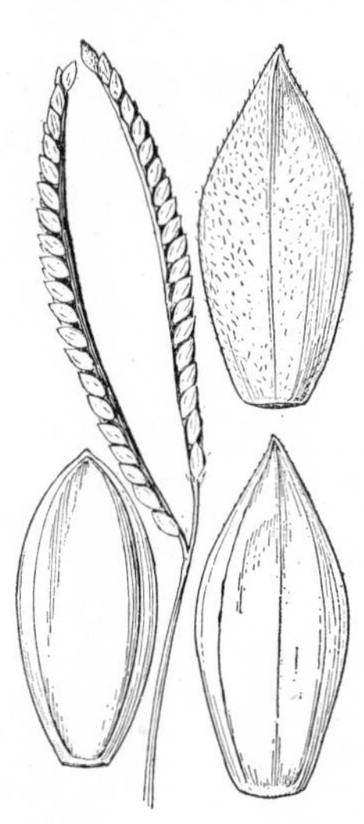

Fig. 26. A Seed Head of *Paspalum distichum. Courtesy of United States Department of Agriculture.*

It is also known as joint grass and Fort Thompson grass. It is found on the Pacific coast from Washington, south through California and Mexico, and in the West Indies, Argentina and Chili. Like other pasture grasses, its value is greatly lessened on poor soils. It is a valuable soil binder.

Paspalum lividum.—This plant has some value as a grazing crop, but due to its habits of growth it would not be adapted to continuous grazing, and would probably disappear after a season or two if closely grazed. *P. lividum* is found in scattered areas along the Gulf Coast. It prefers low areas, and is frequently found growing in the water along irrigation ditches in the rice growing area. Little is known regarding its value as a forage crop.

P. lividum puts out runners sometimes reaching from four to six feet in length and often rooting at the joints. The seed head, or inflorescence, usually has four to seven racemes, but sometimes as low as three or as many as ten, on ascending stems two or three feet high. They are set on a very slender axis, at distances apart on the axis equal to about half their own length. The rachis or backbone of the flower cluster is a dark livid purple. The seed are produced in abundance, and are easily harvested. *P. lividum* should be introduced on lowlands that are moist during the greater part of the spring and summer. It is a smooth perennial, and can be propagated from roots or clumps. It is sensitive to frost. It occurs from Alabama to Texas, and south to Argentina, as well as in Cuba.

Fig. 27. *Paspalum lividum.*

Paspalum hartwegianum.—Also known as *Paspalum buckleyanum,* this species has been grown to some extent in Mississippi as a forage grass. It is a perennial found in southern Texas near the seacoast, and in Mexico. It is found on the better drained alkaline prairies near the beach as well as in the marshes. It produces seed freely and is of some value as a pasture grass where adapted.

Field Paspalum.—(*Paspalum laeve.*) In parts of the South this plant is grazed. Although occurring on waste ground, it is cut for hay, and is considered of value for this purpose.

It is found in eastern Texas and east to Florida, as well as along the Atlantic Coast northward to Pennsylvania and New Jersey. It seems to be adapted to a rather wide range of climatic and soil conditions. It requires about the same conditions for successful growth as Dallis grass.

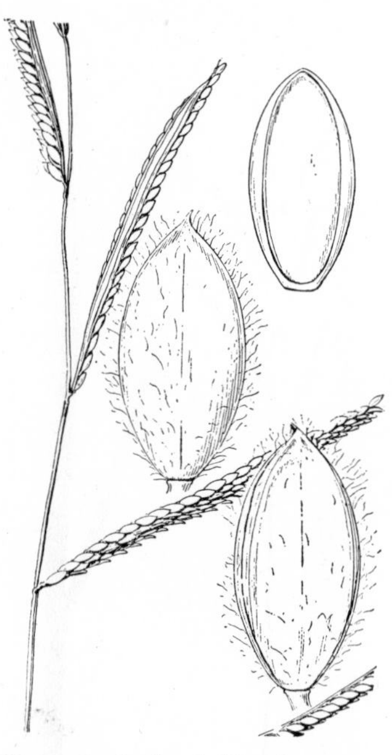

Fig. 28. A Seed Head of *Paspalum hartwegianum. Courtesy of Chase, United States Department of Agriculture.*

Field Paspalum is a tufted perennial with ascending seed stems fifteen to thirty-six inches tall. The seed heads usually have three or four racemes, but occasionally have as few as two or as many as eight. This species has been found to be exceedingly variable.

Ciliate Paspalum.—(*Paspalum ciliatifolium.*) This species is found from Florida to Texas, and also on the Atlantic Coast northward to New Jersey. It has some value as a pasture crop, occurring mostly on sandy soils. It is of more or less importance in Georgia where it is found scattered over the hill pastures, affording some grazing.

Paspalum setaceum.—This species is also found in Georgia pastures, where it grows on soils too poor for Bermuda grass.[3] It occurs on sandy soils in parts of the Gulf Coast, and along the Atlantic coastal plain northward to New York. *Paspalum supinum* is also mentioned as being of some value for grazing. It is a spreading tufted perennial with coarse foliage.

Fig. 29. Field Paspalum.

Bull Grass.—(*Paspalum boscianum.*) This annual Paspalum furnishes grazing in the southeastern states where it is also used for hay. It is considered a valuable grass for dairy cattle, being succulent and nutritious, but it is difficult to cure for hay. Bull grass makes a heavy volunteer growth when started on cultivated lands, coming up after cultivation of crops has ceased and reseeding freely. It is also known as purple paspalum. Bull grass prefers moist open ground, but occurs frequently in cul-

[3] Paul Tabor and E. D. Alexander, *Pastures for Georgia,* Extension Bulletin 389, Athens, Ga.

tivated fields from Virginia to Florida and westward to Louisiana.

Paspalum pubiflorum.—This plant, while found largely in alkaline clay soils of a moist nature, is considered a good drouth-resisting pasture grass in the lower South and middle Cotton Belt. It is a perennial grass with seed stems from fifteen to forty inches high with from two to eight racemes in the seed head.

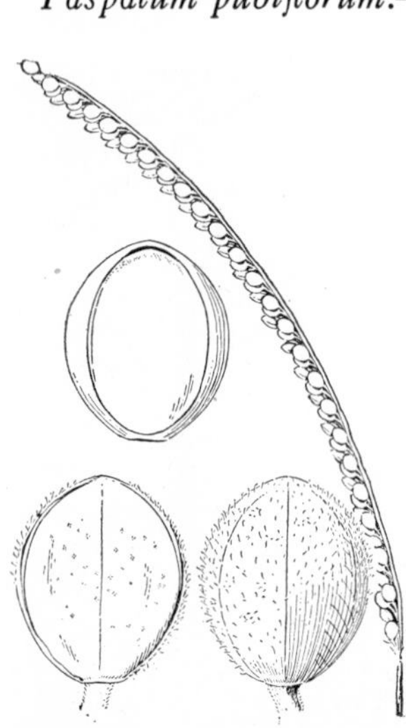

Fig. 30. A Seed Head of *Ciliate Paspalum. Courtesy of Chase, United States Department of Agriculture.*

Paspalum circulare.—This species furnishes excellent grazing, and is found over a wide area and under a rather wide range of conditions. It is a tufted perennial with ascending seed stems from fifteen to forty inches tall. It is sometimes mistaken for *Paspalum laeve,* especially if grown on poor or dry soils. It is a palatable and nutritious pasture grass, well worthy of a place in pastures throughout the Cotton Belt. It occurs as far north as Indiana, in the southern part of which state it has been found to have an important place in native pastures.

Paspalum pubescens.—This species furnishes excellent grazing from the Middle Western States southward, wherever found. It is mostly a late summer and fall grass. It is a perennial, forming dense tufts, with ascending seed

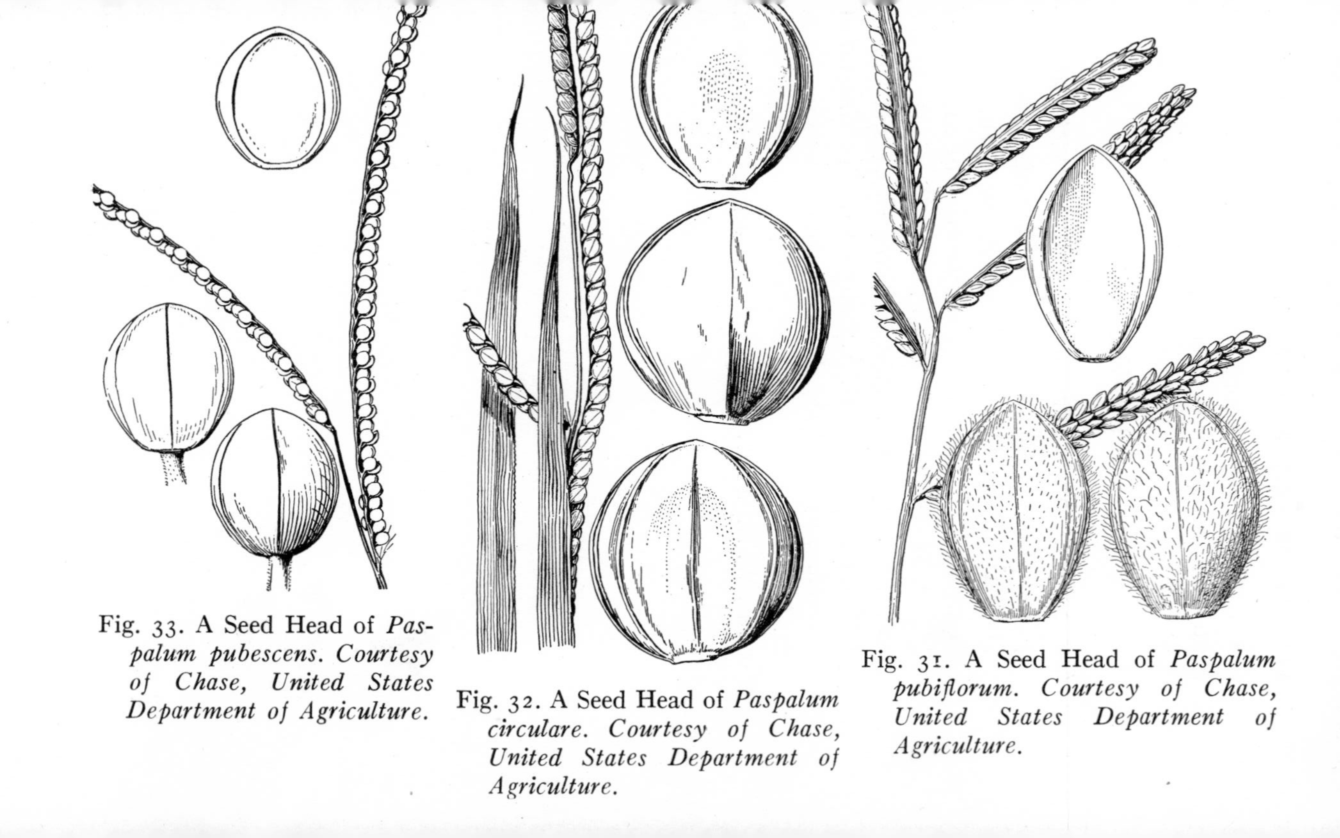

Fig. 33. A Seed Head of *Paspalum pubescens*. Courtesy of Chase, United States Department of Agriculture.

Fig. 32. A Seed Head of *Paspalum circulare*. Courtesy of Chase, United States Department of Agriculture.

Fig. 31. A Seed Head of *Paspalum pubiflorum*. Courtesy of Chase, United States Department of Agriculture.

stems from fifteen to forty inches high. The seed heads have from one to three racemes.

REFERENCES

Chase, Mrs. Agnes, *The North American Species of Paspalum* (Contributions from the United States National Herbarium, vol. 28, pt. 1), Washington, 1929.

Hitchcock, A. S., *Manual of the Grasses of the United States,* Miscellaneous Publication 200, U. S. D. A.

Piper, Chas. V., *Important Cultivated Grasses,* Farmer's Bulletin 1254, U. S. D. A.; and, *Cultivated Grasses of Secondary Importance,* Farmer's Bulletin 1433, U. S. D. A.

Silveus, W. A., *Texas Grasses,* San Antonio, Texas, 1933.

Chapter VII

PASTURE GRASSES OF THE SOUTH

Common Bermuda Grass.—(*Cynodon dactylon.*) Bermuda grass is by far the most important pasture grass in the South. It is adapted to practically all conditions, both as to soil and climate, in the southern states and has spread spontaneously to all parts of the Cotton Belt, making up a large part of the grazing in most southern pastures.

Bermuda grass is palatable and is relished by all livestock. Its persistence and turf-forming qualities give it a place in southern pastures that cannot be taken by any other grass known at this time. With practically no attention, Bermuda will take care of itself under all conditions where it is not shaded with other crops. Farmers have found that one of the best ways to exterminate it in cultivated fields is to shade it by planting crops with heavy foliage, such as velvet beans, for a season or two.

Bermuda grass makes an excellent pasture either alone or in mixture. Close grazing improves its quality, as the stems become unpalatable with age. It grows well with Lespedeza, and follows winter growing clovers such as White Dutch, bur, medic, hop and Persian exceptionally well. Rye grass is often used with Bermuda in the South, the Bermuda taking the place of the Rye grass naturally

Fig. 34. A Well Managed Bermuda Grass Pasture in the Lov
South. Notice the uniformity of the turf. *Courtesy of E*
tension Service, United States Department of Agricultu

as the latter disappears in late spring. Bermuda being a turf-forming grass makes it an important addition to mixtures of such bunch grasses as Dallis and Vasey.

Bermuda grass is best adapted to the Cotton Belt. It has survived winters farther north, but its usefulness for a grazing crop in sections north of the Cotton Belt is limited and such crops as Kentucky bluegrass and Red Top will hold a more important place in the pasture program. It grows on all types of soil, but makes its best growth on loams that are well drained. Loamy bottom lands that are well drained are especially suited to growing Bermuda. Bermuda grows on the poorest soils of the South. It is of little value, however, on sandy soils, being best adapted to loams, silts and clays.

Bermuda is easily killed by frost, and for this reason its usefulness as a grazing crop extends over the period of warm spring, summer and fall weather. It is often injured by the sun in midsummer when moisture is scarce, but recovers soon after rains occur.

Bermuda grass is usually started from small pieces of sod, or parts of the runners. These may be pressed into the soil every three or four feet, or dropped in furrows and lightly covered. This method is satisfactory on small pasture areas.

Bermuda is a low growing perennial, with both underground root stocks and surface runners that take root at the joints. The seed stems are usually from six to twelve inches tall with from three to six spikes. It was introduced into the United States about 1800.

Carpet Grass.—(*Axonopus compressus.*) Carpet grass is next to Bermuda in importance in southern pastures. It is found throughout the South and, when once started, stands its own with other pasture plants, soon forming a dense carpet that supplies an abundance of nutritious grazing. Like Bermuda it is palatable and is relished by all livestock. It endures trampling well and spreads of its own accord on grazing lands, which is an important consideration in pasture development on a large scale. Carpet grass is outstanding as a pasture grass for the moist lands of the cut-over pine area of the South.

Carpet grass has been used with success through the South. Experiments, notably at the Coastal Plain Experiment Station, McNeill, Mississippi, show that carpet grass when well established with Lespedeza will carry at the rate of one head of cattle to one and one-half acres for a period of nine months in the year. On moist soils with fair fertility the carrying capacity may be even better than this. It is difficult to introduce Lespedeza and other legumes where the grass has become established, because of the density of the turf. Disking is usually necessary in planting clovers on carpet grass sod.

Although carpet grass is found on both clay and loam soils, it shows a preference for sandy or loamy land where moisture remains near the surface, and succeeds best on soils where moisture is plentiful most of the growing season. It is better adapted to wet sour soils than Bermuda, and will afford grazing over a longer period during the year, thriving under hot, humid conditions.

Carpet grass is started from the seed. Seed is available in quantity at moderate prices. It is a common practice to sow five or ten pounds of seed to the acre broadcast without seed bed preparation or covering. If the soil is not densely covered with vegetation, this method will give a good start of the grass. A better plan, however, is to prepare the seed bed two or three months in advance of the planting date by breaking or disking, allowing time

Dairy Cattle on Carpet Grass Pasture, Jefferson County, Texas. Fig. 35.

for the soil to become firm. The seeds require a firm soil for germination and growth. February and March plantings are to be preferred. A dense sod may not be formed until the second season from the seeding.

Carpet grass is easily eradicated by plowing. It is a low growing perennial with flattened stems and short blunt pointed leaves of a light green shade. The stems or stolons take root at the joints. The slender seed stems are erect and from twelve to twenty-four inches high. It is called gazon grass in parts of Louisiana.

Cord Grass.—(*Spartina Sp.*) Although abundant only in a relatively small area of the South, in the salt marshes of the coastal prairie near the Gulf of Mexico, the cord grasses are important forage plants of that region because of the large herds of range cattle that graze them during the winter months.

During the summer months when no cattle or other livestock are grazing the cord grasses, they make a coarse growth and become stemmy and unpalatable. Stockmen overcome this condition by burning the grasses during the summer months. Burning does not injure the roots of the grasses, and by early winter a new tender growth is ready to be grazed. Although they remain green during the summer, as well as in the winter, they burn readily when set on fire.

No attempt has been made to propagate cord grass from the seed or to introduce it to new areas, although the United States Department of Agriculture has attempted to get a similar grass, *Spartina townsendii,* which has been very successfully used in the marshes of Holland and England, started in this country. The attempt has not yet been successful.

The cord grasses spread spontaneously to areas adapted

attle Grazing Cord Grass in the Gulf Coast Region of exas. Fig. 36.

to their growth. No doubt seed of these species could be used for propagating purposes.

The most common species along the Gulf Coast are *Spartina spartinae* and *Spartina patens,* although others are found. In some localities they are incorrectly called salt grasses.

Pifine.—(*Panicum hemitomon.*) Pifine, or paille finne as it is sometimes called, occurs in many parts of the Gulf Coast in the low open prairies which are not overflowed by high tides or frequent flood waters. It is most abundant in southern Louisiana where it has been found valuable for hay and grazing, but it is found along the Gulf Coast in small or irregular tracts from Florida to Texas.

It is nearly equal to alfalfa in nutritive value, a rare quality for grass. Chemical analyses have shown the protein content to range from approximately 6% to 10% depending upon the stage at which the plant is cut. The fat content at the most palatable stage is in excess of 2%.

As a grazing crop, pifine is very palatable if grazed closely enough to prevent the grass from reaching the mature stage. It is not injured by moderate grazing. It is not found on the brackish soils but occurs only on lowlands where moisture is reasonably abundant.

Pifine rarely makes seed, but is a perennial, coming back from year to year from the underground root stocks. It is easily propagated from plants or root stocks. Plantings from the roots will be more successful if done before the spring growth begins. The root cuttings or portions of plants should be put out at intervals of a few feet.

Centipede Grass.—(*Eremochloa ophiuroides.*) One of the most promising turf grasses of recent introduction for grazing in the lower South is centipede grass. It is similar in appearance and habits of growth to carpet grass, having no underground runners to become a pest. In some sections of the South, notably at the Coastal Plain Experiment Station, McNeill, Mississippi, and the Florida Experiment Station at Gainesville, the grass is proving highly satisfactory as a grazing crop, covering the ground more rapidly than carpet grass, especially on dry hill lands. In Florida it is used extensively as a lawn grass where it has been found adapted to high dry soils. It is palatable and nutritious and has promise of becoming one of the most popular grazing crops for permanent pastures in the lower South. It will take the place of carpet grass on the drier soils, and will also grow on any other soil where drainage is good.

Fig. 37. A Stolon of Centipede Grass.

Centipede grass makes a dense smooth turf, making it an ideal grass for lawns. It recuperates quickly after severe drouths, and on high dry Norfolk sand in Florida has crowded out all other grasses including Bermuda.[1]

[1] C. R. Enlow and W. E. Stokes, *Lawns in Florida,* Bulletin 209, Fla. Exp. Sta.

Centipede grass makes seed in fair quantity, but the seed crop is difficult to harvest. It is usually propagated from rooted runners. When once established it holds its own with other grasses. It has short leaves growing from two to four inches high. It was introduced into the United States from China in 1918.

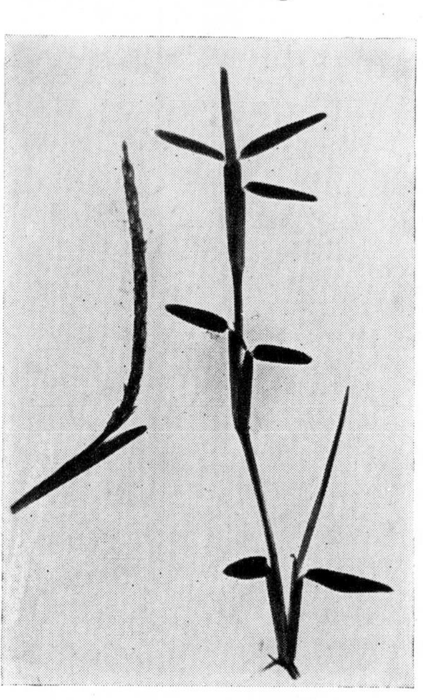

Fig. 38. A Stolon and Seed Head of St. Augustine Grass.

St. Augustine Grass.—(*Stenotaphrum secundatum.*) St. Augustine grass is one of the best turf grasses for shaded areas. It has been used largely for shaded lawns where moisture is abundant and the soil is fertile. In Florida it is the most common lawn grass. For shaded areas in the lower South where moisture is plentiful, this grass will make a valuable addition to the grazing program. While little is known of its value for pasture, its persistence under mowing, and its adaptability to shaded areas, give it an important place in pasture development. Many pastures in the lower South can be improved with such a grass, filling the same need as orchard grass in the upper South.

While St. Augustine grass will grow in continual shade, it requires a continuous supply of moisture and fertile soil. It is coarse but very tender and palatable, forming a dense turf. It spreads by surface runners and, while it makes some seed, is usually propagated by rooted runners.

Texas Bluegrass.—(*Poa arachnifera.*) Texas bluegrass has not held an important place in the southern grazing program, but its adaptability to a wide range of soil and climatic conditions makes it worthy of consideration for wider use. It is a little more bunchy in habit than its relative, Kentucky bluegrass, and makes a larger growth, but is not as persistent in its growing habits. It is sometimes crowded out by southern turf grasses such as Bermuda.

Some effort has been made to cross Texas bluegrass with Kentucky bluegrass in the hope of getting an improvement, but the hybrids so far have been self-sterile, although some showed excellent forage qualities.

Texas bluegrass is a perennial native to Texas and Oklahoma. It grows from one to two feet high, with seed heads or panicles from two to four inches long. It has slender underground root stocks, or rhizomes. It can be propagated by planting divisions of the old clumps. The seeds of this grass are small and silky and are best gathered by stripping. It is adapted to fall planting for winter and spring pasture, and endures the hot sun well.

Kikuyu Grass.—(*Pennisetum clandestinum.*) Kikuyu grass was introduced into the South by the United States Department of Agriculture, in the hope that it would prove valuable for the Gulf States. For some reason not yet fully determined the Kikuyu grass contracts a leaf disorder and dies from the center of the bunch outward, the older portions of the plant first showing the trouble. When affected with this trouble the leaves turn yellow and the grass loses its vigor, practically ceasing growth.

Kikuyu grass was introduced from the highlands of east Africa where it is considered to be one of the best pasture grasses for rich moist soil. Glowing reports regarding its pasture value have come also from Australia.

Kikuyu grass is similar to Bermuda grass in its habits of growth, having trailing stems that root at the joints. It prefers a moist soil, and can be propagated from rooted runners.

Giant Bermuda.—(*Cynodon dactylon* var.) This giant strain of Bermuda has been found adapted to practically all conditions where common Bermuda grows. It is a larger species than the common variety, but is otherwise very much like it. In the lower South, it has shown a rapid growth on heavy soils as well as loams. When portions of the runners are planted five feet each way it soon covers the ground. This grass will be found useful wherever a larger variety of Bermuda is desired. It is propagated by setting out parts of the parent plants.

A variety of Giant Bermuda (*Cynodon dactylon* var. *maritimus*) is used to a limited extent for permanent pastures in Florida. It occurs in Florida mainly along the east coast, and in such locations is found successful in permanent pasture mixtures. It seems to do a little better on low damp land than the ordinary strain of Bermuda. Seed of this variety cannot be obtained in quantity, and this necessitates vegetative plantings, using the same methods as for the common Bermuda.

St. Lucie Grass.—(*Cynodon dactylon* var.) St. Lucie grass is a species of Bermuda that does not have underground root stocks. It is used to some extent, and with very satisfactory results, in Florida on the east coast and in parts of the Everglades. Its habit of growth, and the fact that it is more easily eradicated than common Ber-

nuda, should cause it to increase in popularity. Its adap-
ations are not well known, but it is apparently adapted
o the Cotton Belt. Its use as a pasture grass is at the
resent time limited to parts of Florida. There is no
eed of this species on the market, and this necessitates
egetative plantings.

Buffalo Grass.—(*Buchloe dactyloides.*) Buffalo grass
s an important grazing plant in the Great Plains region.
Vhere it grows alone it forms a close grayish green turf
hat is highly esteemed by ranchmen of that area for
grazing livestock. It grows well on the uplands of the
"short grass country," and may well be included in pas-
ure mixtures in the plains region of Texas and Oklahoma.
Seed of this grass cannot be obtained commercially, and
his necessitates vegetative plantings. Rooted portions of
he plants may be set in the soil at intervals over the
pasture lands in early spring when moisture is plentiful.

Star Grass.—(*Cynodon plectostachyus.*) Star grass, a
native of tropical Africa, has been tried in some parts
of the lower South, and found to be successful. It has long
surface runners but no root stocks. It is sensitive to frost.

Igoka Grass.—This is a related species very much like
star grass in habit. It has done well in parts of the lower
South. It is also a native of tropical Africa.

Transvaal Kweek Grass.—(*Cynodon incompletus.*)
This species of cynodon has been tried in a limited way in
the southern states, and has some promise as a forage
plant. Its range of usefulness is not yet known in the
South.

Giant Carpet Grass.—(*Axonopus furcatus.*) This species is very similar to common carpet grass, except that it
grows more erect and has larger spikelets. It has not
become of any economic importance, but because of its

palatability and adaptability to a wide range of soil and climatic conditions, it is worthy of consideration for a pasture plant.

Giant carpet grass will grow in partly shaded areas and grows under practically the same soil and moisture conditions as carpet grass. It produces seed freely on erect seed stems from twelve to thirty inches high. The seed head is always forked (furcated) and is easily distinguished from common carpet grass, the two racemes of the seed head being equal in length and sometimes as long as four inches. It is more succulent than carpet grass and could be utilized to advantage on moist, partly shaded areas in the lower South. It has about the same range as ordinary carpet grass, but is not as common. It is found in scattered areas in Texas, Louisiana and other Gulf States.

Molasses Grass.—(*Melinis minutiflora.*) Molasses grass has been used to some extent in parts of the lower South along the Gulf of Mexico. The grass is covered with small hairs that secrete a sweet substance with an odor like molasses. The excretion is present soon after the grass begins growth, and continues on the blades and stems throughout the growing season. It is very nutritious, but the odor is somewhat objectionable to livestock until they have acquired a taste for it.

Molasses grass is nutritious and is highly esteemed as a pasture grass in central Brazil. It is also utilized for hay. Plantings in the lower Gulf Coast do not survive the winter if the temperature falls far below freezing. However, it is of some value in southern Florida and the Rio Grande Valley of Texas, where temperatures are favorable to its growth. It grows from two to four feet high.

Molasses grass seeds freely. Spring plantings are ready
o graze by early summer, and the grass soon completely
overs the ground with a dense mat of fine stems that take
oot at the joints. The seeds are very small. Four or five
ounds to the acre, planted on a well prepared seed bed
nd very lightly cov-
red, will give a good
tand. It seeds from
Iay to November.

It is a native of trop-
cal Africa, and is cul-
ivated in Hawaii, the
hilippines, South Af-
ica, Australia and the
Vest Indies. It is also
nown as stink grass,
ordura grass, honey
rass and Efwatakala.
t is adapted to loamy
oils. Molasses grass is
perennial, and can
e propagated from
ooted runners, as well
s from the seed.

Fig. 39. A Seed Head of Molasses Grass.

*Kentucky Blue-
rass.*—(*Poa praten-
is.*) Kentucky bluegrass is the most noted pasture grass
n North America. It is commonly used for lawns, and
hrives in partial shade, making it popular for this pur-
ose. This habit contributes to its spread into open woods,
n localities where the summers are hot and dry, furnish-
ng valuable pasture.

Kentucky bluegrass is only adapted to parts of the

upper South and northward. Further south it is not successful in pasture mixtures.

Kentucky bluegrass is a long-lived perennial with creeping underground stems, with each having a tuft of leaves at the tip. The leaves are long, slender and drooping, of a waxy green appearance.

Fall sowing has proved best. If a quick stand is desired, from twenty-five to thirty pounds of seed are used, while twelve to twenty pounds may be sufficient to get a fair stand under favorable conditions.

Red Top.—(*Agrostis alba.*) Few grasses will grow under as great a variety of conditions as Red Top. For the upper South it is the best wet-land grass among the many species used for pasture, and is second only to Kentucky bluegrass in importance. It does not survive the hot summer in the lower South sufficiently well to hold an important place in pasture programs.

Red Top is tolerant to acid soils, and will grow in water or shallow ponds for weeks. It can be utilized to advantage for grazing in low bottom lands and does not show any particular soil preference, if moisture is abundant. Alsike clover is an excellent legume to use with Red Top because of its adaptability to wet soils. White Dutch clover is also used with it to advantage.

Red Top is a long-lived perennial, with erect seed stems usually about two feet high. The seed head is an open panicle from two to twelve inches long, varying in color from greenish to purple or brown. It has underground rhizomes, or root stocks, that enable the grass to grow new plants thickening the sod, one of the reasons for its popularity in pasture mixtures.

Red Top is best adapted to plantings with other crops. In regions where adapted it is aggressive and will spread turally. It is a vigorous grower and forms a turf in a ort time. In mixture with other grasses, four or five ounds of seed to the acre will be sufficient. If seeded one, from ten to fifteen pounds should be used, planting roadcast in the early fall. Soil preparation is not always ecessary. If plenty of seeds are used, they may be lanted directly on the sod without covering. If the soil prepared, it should be firm at planting time and the ed covered very shallow.

Orchard Grass.—(Dactylis glomerata.) Orchard grass one of the most popular grasses for both pasture and ay. Its adaptability to shaded areas has given rise to its ame, and it is often used for planting in areas too shaded r other species. This habit makes it of considerable alue for planting in the open wooded areas where other rasses do not prove profitable. It is palatable and nutri-ous to livestock.

Orchard grass is a bunch grass, and is not adapted to lanting alone for grazing. In mixtures with turf-forming rasses, it will be found much more satisfactory than hen planted alone. It is also a valuable hay grass.

Orchard grass is more sensitive to cold than timothy, ut will withstand hot weather for a longer period. It ill grow on practically all soil types, but prefers clays r clay loams, with a moderate amount of moisture. Spring lantings are to be preferred, although it may be planted the fall. Spring plantings may not come to seed the rst year, but where adapted will persist for an indefinite eriod.

It is frequently sown with wheat in the fall. For hay, rom ten to fifteen pounds of clean seed are required, hile from five to eight pounds to the acre will be suffi-ient in mixtures. It can be planted in the fall on sod

land without seed bed preparation, but more seed shoul
be used where this is done. It is also planted in the sprin
with oats or barley as nurse crops.

Orchard grass is a long-lived perennial bunch grass
with no underground root stocks. It never forms a com
plete sod.

Canada Bluegrass.—(*Poa compressa.*) In many case
acreages too poor for cultivation are used as pasture
Hillsides, made poor by erosion, are frequently used fo
grazing. In cases of this kind, north of the Cotton Bel
and in parts of the upper South, Canada bluegrass is we
worth considering for a grazing crop. Its ability to su
vive under unfavorable soil conditions gives it an impo
tant place in pasture planting programs in the hill
section.

Sheep Fescue.—(*Festuca ovina.*) Sheep fescue is
valuable pasture grass for poor sandy or gravelly lan
in parts of the upper South. Although tough and appa
ently unpalatable, it is nutritious and readily grazed whe
used in mixtures with other grazing crops. In the uppe
South, sheep fescue fits successfully into a pasture pro
gram for poor hilly land that is to be utilized for grazin
It will thrive on land too poor for the common cultivate
varieties to succeed. It survives heavy grazing and tran
pling, being deep rooted. It is much more palatable
grazed closely.

In mixtures with other grasses, from five to ten pounc
of seed to the acre will be sufficient, while from twent
to twenty-five will be necessary when planted alone. O
fertile soils, other varieties should always be used, an
sheep fescue added only where conditions warrant its us

Meadow Fescue.—(*Festuca elatior.*) While of relativel
small importance as a pasture plant, meadow fescue ca

be used to advantage in many instances. It is adapted to growing in mixture with other pasture crops in the upper South, beginning its growth in early spring and continuing until late fall.

The grass is planted on a well-prepared seed bed, either in the fall or spring, using from five to ten pounds of seed to the acre in mixtures. If planted alone, from ten to fifteen pounds of seed are used to the acre for producing a seed crop. Heavy seedings are said to reduce the seed crops, but are to be preferred for hay or grazing.

Red Fescue.—(Festuca rubra.) Red fescue has been used mainly for lawns, but its habits of growth make it of some value in pasture plantings in the upper South. It is especially adapted to sandy and gravelly soils, and will grow satisfactorily in partly shaded areas.

The usual rate of seeding is from twenty-five to thirty pounds to the acre. Spring plantings will probably be the best.

Sweet Vernal Grass.—(Anthoxanthum odoratum.) Sweet vernal grass can be utilized to some advantage in the upper South as a supplemental grazing crop with other grasses. Its earliness and adaptability to poor lands may justify its use on soils where more palatable species will not grow. Its peculiar odor and bitter taste prevent livestock from grazing it until they acquire a taste for it. Its odor is due to the coumarin, a rather unusual quality, which the grass contains. It is very sweet scented while drying. Its chief advantage in the upper South is its ability to grow under soil conditions where the fertility is too low for other grasses of equal value.

From four to eight pounds of seed to the acre are recommended. It is doubtful if plantings are justified where conditions are favorable to any of the other common pasture grasses of the upper South. Sweet vernal grass is a native of Europe.

Bird Grass.—(*Poa trivialis.*) Bird grass is adapted to the Kentucky bluegrass region, and will not survive the hot sun south of that area sufficiently to warrant its use as a pasture plant. In the region where adapted it is an excellent pasture grass.

It is best adapted to grazing when mixed with other grasses. When planted for pasture, from two to fifteen pounds of seed to the acre should be planted. Either fall or spring seedings can be made.

REFERENCES

A Handbook of Agronomy, Extension Bulletin 97, V. P. I., Blacksburg, Va.

Duggar, J. F., *Southern Forage Crops,* New York, 1925.

Jeffords, S. L., *Better Pastures for South Carolina,* Extension Circular 67, Clemson College, S. C.

Kinney, E. J., Kenny, Ralph, and Fergus, E. N., *Practices in Seeding Meadow and Pasture Crops,* Extension Circular 242, Lexington, Ky.

Lowery, J. C., *Pasture Suggestions,* Extension Circular 110, Auburn, Ala.

Piper, C. V., *Forage Plants and Their Culture,* New York, 1914.

Semple, A. T., Vinall, H. N., Enlow, C. W., and Woodward, T. E., *A Pasture Handbook,* Miscellaneous Publication 194, U. S. D. A.

Wasson, R. A., *Pasture and Forage Crops for Louisiana,* Extension Circular 140, Baton Rouge, La.

Chapter VIII

SUPPLEMENTAL PASTURE AND HAY GRASSES

Sudan Grass.—(*Sorghum vulgare,* var. *sudanensis.*) Sudan grass is the most widely cultivated hay plant on the farms of the middle and lower South. It is also grown extensively by dairy farmers as a green fodder plant. On fertile lands with a reasonable moisture supply, Sudan produces a good yield of forage that is both palatable and nutritious. On account of its fine stems, it cures into hay readily.

Sudan grass is also utilized as a summer grazing crop. It is an excellent grass for this purpose and, if planted in the spring, under favorable conditions will carry one cow to an acre for a period of three months during the season.

Close grazing is injurious to Sudan if it is continuous. The best method of grazing is one which provides for two or more alternating pastures, allowing grazed areas to have a period of rest to make new growth. The summer Sudan pasture works into a system of permanent pasture utilization exceptionally well. Livestock can be turned on the Sudan pasture in June or July when it is fifteen or twenty inches high, and this allows the permanent pasture a period of rest.

Sudan thrives during the hottest days of summer when permanent pastures are suffering for lack of moisture. If

Fig. 40. Dairy Cattle Grazing Supplemental Pasture of Su Grass. *Courtesy of Extension Service, United Sta Department of Agriculture.*

not grazed too closely, the carrying capacity will remain high until frost. Close grazing greatly reduces the number of grazing days during the season. This is due largely to the injury caused by disturbing the root system. Cattle in grazing the plant pull it hard enough to break loose many of the feed roots. The plant will recover from this if allowed to grow a week or two without grazing. As a crop to cut and feed green, Sudan is ideal. It produces a larger tonnage when utilized in this manner than when grazed, and can be cut two or three times during the season.

Experimental work covering several seasons at Woodward, Oklahoma, established the fact that, for that locality, Sudan would furnish more nutrients per acre during the summer months than any other pasture grass. It withstood the lack of moisture and hot winds better than any other grass. In these experiments the Sudan was clipped every thirty days, and the weights of the green grass were estimated from the yields of dry matter. The following table, supplied by the United States Department of Agriculture, gives in concise form the results of these experiments.

Sudan hay is cured easily. In the humid region of the lower South, Sudan should be cut with a binder and shocked within a few hours after cutting. In this way it can be cured into a good quality hay. If cut and allowed to stay on the ground, it will be difficult to cure. In the Gulf Coast region, Gulf breezes laden with moisture often cause a heavy dew making it difficult to cure Sudan hay, especially where it is allowed to lie on the ground at night.

Reports of poisoning from grazing Sudan are extremely rare. This possibility is so remote as to make it negligible.

Sudan is closely related to the other sorghums, and is known as a grass sorghum.

TABLE VIII

The effect of precipitation on the yields and carrying capacity of Sudan grass at Woodward, Oklahoma, 1929 and 1930.

Month	*Green grass per acre * Pounds*	*Dry matter per acre Pounds*	*Precipitation Inches*	*Milking cows that could be kept on 10 acres*
SEASON OF 1929				
June	3080	616	.58	7
July	2870	1174	3.15	14
August	1875	375	2.09	4
Sept.	2565	513	4.45	6
SEASON OF 1930				
June	5700	1140	2.93	14
July	3565	713	.23	8
August	3725	745	1.42	9
Sept.	1055	211	1.06	3
AVERAGE OF 1929 AND 1930				
June	4390	878	1.75	10
July	4717	943	1.69	11
August	2800	560	1.75	6
Sept.	1810	362	2.75	4

* Estimated from the dry matter.

Sudan grass is adapted to the entire South, and does well on any soil that will produce a crop of cotton or corn. It should not be planted on poor soils. Like all other sorghums, it will not grow well in cool weather, and should not be planted until the ground is warm in spring. It thrives on both loams and clays. The soil type has far less to do with its success than the fertility of the soil. It survives drouth remarkably well, and will produce good yields under an unfavorable distribution of rainfall. It produces seed wherever sorghums mature seed.

Sudan should be planted on a well-prepared seed bed, as required for other field crops. When planted in rows a cultivation or two will aid in getting a quick growth. As soon as the plants are large enough to shade the ground, cultivation can cease.

Plantings should be made as soon as the soil is warm in spring and danger of frost is past. Sudan can be planted when sorghums and corn are planted. On the average soil early plantings will mature three cuttings of hay in the lower South, two in the middle South and one in the upper South. It requires about sixty days for the grass to reach the stage for hay. Broadcast seedings are common on fertile soil, and this is to be preferred. When planted in rows, from ten to fifteen pounds of seed may be planted. Broadcast seedings require from thirty to forty pounds to the acre. Heavy seedings insure a better stand and prevent other grasses and weeds from making up a large part of the yield.

Sudan grass is an erect annual plant from five to seven feet high, producing stems the size of a pencil. The plants are very much like Johnson grass, but the leaves of Sudan are longer and broader, and the seed heads are from ten to sixteen inches long. There are several types of the grass, some having a higher sugar content than others.

Sudan grass was introduced into the United States in 1908 from Khartoum, Sudan, Africa, by the United States Department of Agriculture.

Johnson Grass.—(*Sorghum halapense.*) Johnson grass is not usually classed as a cultivated grass. It is difficult

Fig. 41. Johnson Grass.

to eradicate when once started on farms of the middle and lower South, where it is known and dreaded as a serious pest in cultivated fields. In fact, prejudice against the grass has prevented its taking a more favorable place in the forage crop program. However, any crop with the persistence and palatability of Johnson grass offers an opportunity to utilize abandoned fields for the production of excellent forage. Only one or two other grasses in the South are utilized to a greater extent for hay. It is not primarily a pasture grass, and does not survive heavy grazing year after year in spite of its persistence. It occurs mainly in cultivated areas or abandoned fields, rarely being found in closely grazed pastures. Heavy stands of the grass disappear from fields turned into pasture in about four seasons. Like other perennial plants, top growth is essential to the development of the underground root stocks and, when closely grazed, the roots die out.

Johnson grass requires the same soil and climatic conditions as cotton. It is a perennial where the winters are not too severe and is rarely killed out by freezes in the South. It requires a reasonably fertile soil, and resists drouthy weather remarkably well.

Where it has already become established, Johnson grass can be made into excellent hay meadows. Under normal conditions the grass makes a quick growth and can be cut three or four times during the season. It makes the best hay when cut while the head is still in the boot or leaf sheath. If allowed to stand longer, the fiber content of the hay is much higher and it is less digestible. Early cutting also removes the possibility of infesting other lands from mature seed in the hay.

Johnson grass can be utilized in the same manner as Sudan. It makes an excellent soiling crop, but the yields are never very high. When brought to the surface by plowing the roots are eagerly eaten by hogs and by other domestic animals.

When Johnson grass becomes stunted by dry weather or frost, it is a possible source of danger to livestock due to prussic acid in the leaves. If the plants are cut and allowed to cure, this danger is eliminated. Poisoning of livestock from Johnson grass is rare, but as in other sorghums, the danger is always present and should be considered.

Johnson grass is not recommended for planting on new

areas in the South because it becomes a pest in cultivated areas. Sudan, a close relative and an annual, is far more desirable.

Where it has become established, it will be better to use it for hay or pasture than to undertake eradication. Infested areas may be seeded to hay or oats for spring grazing. Cowpeas, crimson clover where adapted, and vetch are also suited to growing with Johnson grass. After these crops are mature and cut for hay, another cutting of the grass is possible. Where plantings are desired, from twenty to thirty pounds of seed to the acre broadcast will be sufficient. Johnson grass is a long-lived perennial with underground root stocks. The panicle is open and very much like Sudan. It was introduced into the United States from Turkey about 1830, and took its name from Colonel William Johnson who grew it near Selma, Alabama, about 1840.

Rhodes Grass.—(*Chloris gayana.*) Rhodes grass has become a popular forage plant in the lower South, both for hay and pasture. It is an excellent hay grass, being fine stemmed and very leafy, and has also been used with success as a grazing crop. In the lower South where the temperature does not drop below 18° or 20° F. the grass is a perennial and spreads by means of running branches that take root at the joints, as well as by seed. Farther north the grass is an annual, being completely killed out during the winter, making it necessary to plant it each spring.

Rhodes grass, like other tall growing species, is not adapted to permanent pastures where close grazing and heavy trampling may be expected, unless the area can be reseeded every season. It does well under irrigation, and has been highly satisfactory for a grazing crop on

)airy Cows on Rhodes Grass Pasture, Jim Wells County, 'exas. *Courtesy of Extension Service, United States De-*
›artment of Agriculture. Fig. 42.

fertile soils that have been prepared by breaking an allowed to settle before planting. It is aggressive, pala table and nutritious.

Rhodes grass is best adapted to rich soils of a loam nature where moisture is reasonably plentiful. However it is successful on other types of soil. If intended fo grazing, it may be planted on any soil capable of pro ducing a good crop of corn or cotton. It has furnishe good grazing in the South on black clay soil.

Rhodes grass may be planted either in rows or broad- cast. In parts of the South it has been used as a row crop alternated with corn, and pastured after the corn was removed from the land. When planted in rows with corn, every third row may be planted to the grass at corn planting time, using two pounds of seed to the acre. For broadcast plantings, from ten to twelve pounds of seed to the acre are required. The seed bed for Rhodes grass should be well prepared but firm, and the seed covered very lightly. It should be planted as soon as danger from frost is past in the spring.

Rhodes grass takes its name from Cecil Rhodes, who first cultivated it on his estate at Cape Town, South Africa, about 1895. He found it growing wild in that region. It was introduced into the United States in 1902, the first packet of seed being sent to the United States Department of Agriculture by Messrs. Lathrop and Fair- child, who were interested in introducing plants for hay and forage in this country.[1] It was received under the botanical name of *Chloris virgata*. This mistake, how- ever, was corrected later.

Rhodes grass produces fine seed stems about three feet

[1] R. A. Oakley, "Some New Grasses for the South," U. S. D. A. *Yearbook, 1912*, p. 496.

high, with finger-like seed heads of a dozen or more spikes.

Para Grass.—(*Panicum barbinode.*) Para grass is adapted to conditions in the lower South, and is a valuable crop for lands too wet for other hay and grazing crops. It is a coarse growing grass, but is readily eaten by live-stock and makes a good quality hay if cut before it becomes unpalatable by age. Its habits of growth do not warrant its use on permanent pastures, but it can be utilized to advantage on low wet lands, in marshes, on banks of streams and lakes, and on lands subject to overflow for a considerable period during the season.

This grass makes an excellent crop for cutting and feeding green, and is utilized in this manner to a large extent in Mexico and South America. It is largely cultivated for forage and hay in tropical countries, in both the Eastern and Western hemispheres.

Para grass is adapted to moist lands, but will make a fair growth on drier soils. In the lower South where the temperature rarely drops below 18° F. it behaves as a perennial. Farther north it would be completely killed out, and only one crop could be depended upon from one planting. It will survive on lands under water for several weeks.

Para grass is propagated by planting pieces of the stems or runners. These pieces are cut about a foot long and pushed into the soil at an angle. The runners may be placed in shallow furrows and lightly covered, but care should be used not to cover the stems too deep. Pieces of the stems should be planted from two to four feet apart for best results the first season. The long runners will soon cover the ground and begin a dense upright growth.

Preparation of the soil by plowing will insure a better stand and more successful growth, but the grass may be put out without soil preparation. Plowing the ground every two or three seasons will improve the grass. Cuttings are usually put out in the spring, but may be placed in the soil at any convenient time during the season. Late plantings cannot be expected to make a satisfactory growth the same season, but will make an early start and heavy growth the following spring if the roots survive the winter.

Para grass was first found in Brazil. It is a tropical grass with runners the size of a pencil, sometimes reaching thirty-five or forty feet in length. These runners soon cover the area where planted, and the grass then makes an upright growth from independent plants coming from the rooted joints of the runners. If supported, the grass may reach a height of ten or twelve feet. Seed are produced mostly during the dry season, but shatter badly and are seldom used for planting, the germination being poor.

Carib Grass.—(*Eriochloa subglabra.*) Carib grass is somewhat leafier than Para grass, and for this reason is slightly better suited as a grazing plant. It is so nearly like Para grass that the two are almost indistinguishable and, so far as their agricultural uses are concerned, they are about equal. It has been tried in parts of the Gulf Coast and has given good results. This grass will not withstand either cold or dry weather, and produces runners less extensively than Para grass. It has no advantages over Para grass that would give it any preference in the lower South. It is a native of the West Indies, where it is used quite extensively for forage. In Puerto Rico it is called Malojilla.

Timothy.—(*Phleum pratense*.) Timothy is the most im-
ortant hay grass in the United States, and is used to a
eat extent throughout the North and in the upper
outh. Southward in the Cotton Belt it is not recom-
ended for general cultivation, as it does not survive the
ot summer sun. In the upper South it is a valuable crop
r hay, and will yield heavy crops the first and second
ar.

Timothy prefers fertile clay or loam soil with plenty
moisture, and is next to Red Top in its ability to grow
damp soils. It does not withstand drouth and, for this
ason, its range of usefulness is limited to the humid
gions of the United States north of the Cotton Belt.
hen planted farther south it dies out in summer. Tim-
hy is not adapted to permanent pasture plantings ex-
pt in mixture; however, it is quite desirable for mixtures
temporary pastures.

Timothy is planted in the fall, at the rate of twelve to
teen pounds to the acre on a well-prepared seed bed,
ually with grain. Alsike and red clover are often seeded
th it in the spring. It is sometimes planted on meadows
thout preparation of the soil, and if the soil is fertile
d well drained, it will establish a fair stand in spite of
her grasses. It may also be planted in the spring.

It is a native of Europe and northern Asia, and was
rly introduced into the United States. It is a short-lived
rennial, from two to four feet tall, with elongate cylin-
ic seed heads.

Angleton Grass.—(*Andropogon annulatus*.) Angleton
ass was introduced into the Gulf Coastal Plains in re-
nt years. It has been successful on a wide variety of
ls, from sandy loams to heavy waxy black clay, in
periments, but is not widely used for grazing. Experi-

mental data at hand show that the grass is adapted t climatic conditions approximately two hundred miles nort of the coast of the Gulf of Mexico, and that it has grow well under rainfall of from thirty to more than sixt inches, surviving winter temperatures as low as 10° F At the present time the grass is propagated entirely fror rooted plants or runners, since seed produced in the Gul Coast area are of low germination.

Angleton grass is adapted to the humid part of th Gulf Coastal Plains. It produces best on well-draine soils, and while it thrives under excessive rainfall, it ha remained green during dry months when native grasse were yellow and apparently dead. It holds its own wit other grasses, crowding out Bermuda and Para grass o experimental plots. Its range of usefulness is apparentl limited to regions where the winter temperatures do nc fall below 15° F.

Angleton grass is easily started from rooted runne planted at intervals of from twenty-five to thirty inche It is best to prepare the soil by disking so that the roote plants may be thrust into the loose soil or dropped int a furrow and lightly covered. If cultivation is possibl it will enable the plants to get a quicker start over othe grasses and weeds. The grass soon puts out prostra runners that take root at the joints, forming a turf. Sprin plantings are best, but the plants may be put out at an time moisture and soil conditions are suitable. A heav growth should not be expected from late plantings th first season.

Angleton grass is a native of India, where it is use for hay and grazing. It was first given exhaustive tes by the Angleton Texas Experiment Station, from whic station it takes its name. The grass was furnished th

.ngleton Grass Pasture, Brazoria County, Texas. *Cour-*
:sy of R. H. Stansel, Texas Agricultural Experiment
tation.

Fig. 43.

station by the United States Department of Agricultu
in 1915. In India it is known as Marvel and Jinga gras
It is a perennial with prostrate runners taking root at th
joints that touch the ground, each joint forming an i
dependent plant and sending up leafy stems from thre
to five feet tall. The seed head consists of three or fou
racemes. It does not have root stocks or rhizomes, and i
easily eradicated if desired.

Natal Grass.—(*Tricholaena rosea.*) Natal grass is
special value on poor sandy soils in the lower South, an
grows well on high sand hills where moisture is lackin
for a large part of the season. In Florida where it ha
become an important forage plant on well-drained lan
it perpetuates itself indefinitely and is often a voluntee
crop after early field and vegetable crops are harveste
Natal grass was first used for ornamental purposes, an
was introduced into the United States about 1866.[2]
furnishes good grazing and is relished by livestock.
is also a popular hay plant, yielding two or three cutting
of hay under favorable conditions. This grass may be use
to advantage for both grazing and hay in the lower Sout

Natal grass will not survive freezing weather, and can
not be depended upon for pasture or hay where the winte
temperatures drop below freezing. Duggar says freeze
not only kill the entire plant, but may also destroy th
shattered seed. It may be used to advantage in Florid
and the lower Gulf Coast on sandy well-drained land
its chief advantage for this area being its ability to gro
on poor dry soils.

Natal grass can be planted either in fall or spring, bu
if planted in regions where the winter temperature drop

[2] C. V. Piper, *Cultivated Grasses of Secondary Importanc*
Farmer's Bulletin 1433, U. S. D. A.

ield of Natal Grass. *Courtesy of United States Department of Agriculture.* Fig. 44.

below freezing, it is best to delay plantings until all danger of frost is past in the spring. For best results, from eight to ten pounds of seed to the acre are required. It requires little if any soil preparation or attention.

It is a slender upright grass with attractive purple seed heads from four to ten inches long. It grows in tufts and reaches a height of from two to four feet. It produces flowers from late spring until killed by frost. Natal grass deserves a wider use in the lower South where soil is suited to its growth, and will give profitable returns even where plantings are necessary each spring.

Colorado Grass.—(*Panicum texanum.*) Colorado grass, a native of southern Texas and Louisiana, is of some importance as a forage grass, and could be made to fill a more important place in the lower South for this purpose. This grass is found in cultivated fields in southeastern Texas and southern Louisiana, and is apparently adapted to conditions throughout the lower South, where the soil is reasonably fertile and well drained. It is leafy and palatable, and makes a quick growth. In cultivated fields where it is usually found, it comes up after the last cultivation and matures its seed crop before frost. It is not regarded as a serious pest in fields because its growth usually takes place after the crops are practically matured. During the fall, it furnishes excellent grazing after the crops are removed.

Colorado grass makes a good quality hay, and is a desirable crop for hay on cultivated areas. It does not survive on sod lands.

The grass reaches a height of two or three feet, sometimes more. The seeds shatter badly unless the grass is cut early. For hay or temporary summer pastures, after danger of frost is past, from twenty-five to thirty pounds of seed to the acre should be planted on a well-prepared but firm seed bed and lightly covered. This grass is sometimes called Texas millet. It is common in the valley of the Colorado river in Texas, where it was first called Colorado grass. It is rarely found on uncultivated lands.

Crab Grass.—(*Syntherisma sanguinalis.*) Every farmer in the South is acquainted with crab grass, for it is the most common pest in cultivated fields. It is not utilized as a forage grass as often as it could be, and on most farms it comes up as a volunteer crop. Its free seeding habit enables it to spread rapidly, and it comes to a good stand early in the spring on practically all cultivated fields. It is never planted because all that is required on most loamy soils of the South for a stand of the grass is to plow and level the land for the mower.

Crab grass does not produce heavy yields of hay, but the quality is good and because of the small stems it is easily cured. A grass with the persistence of crab grass should be utilized for forage to a greater extent. In this way the efforts directed at ridding the fields of the grass will be repaid with a good quality of hay. It will not endure heavy grazing, and is killed by the first frosts. It is common in pastures and lawns.

Tall Meadow Oat Grass.—(*Arrhenatherum elatius.*) Tall meadow oat grass is adapted to a wide range of seasonal weather changes, growing from the Gulf of Mexico to the northern limit of the orchard grass region. It is one of the most drouth resistant of the cultivated grasses, and gives excellent yields of hay or green forage on soils too poor for most other species to grow well. As a hay or grazing crop on poor soils, tall meadow oat grass is well worthy of a place. It does best in mixtures with other grasses and clovers. Orchard grass is most com-

Fig. 45. A Plot of Tall Meadow Oat Grass at Arlington Farm Virginia. *Courtesy of Extension Service, United State Department of Agriculture.*

monly used with tall meadow oat grass, for both hay and grazing. Red and alsike clovers are desirable legumes to use in combination with the grass.

Tall meadow oat grass should be used in the middle and upper South, especially in the drier regions, and on the poorer soils where success with other important cultivated grasses is not assured. It will not grow on wet or shaded areas. It is a perennial with seed stems from three to four feet high, the seed head being from six to ten inches long. In mixtures, from ten to twenty pounds of seed to the acre are required. Fall seeding will be best in most cases. This grass remains green most of the year in the South, except in the Gulf Coast humid region, where it languishes in the summer. It is sometimes called evergreen grass.

REFERENCES

Fain, J. R., and Tabor, Paul, *Hay Crops for Georgia*, Extension Bulletin 237, Athens, Ga.

Hafner, V. E., *Angleton Grass*, Bulletin 342, Agr. Exp. Sta., College Station, Texas.

Karper, R. E., Quinby, J. R., and Jones, D. L., *Sudan Grass for Hay, Seed and Pasture*, Bulletin 396, Agr. Exp. Sta., College Station, Texas.

Pollock, E. O., *Johnson Grass in Texas*, Circular 43, Agr. Exp. Sta., College Station, Texas.

Tracy, S. M., *Rhodes Grass*, Farmer's Bulletin 1048, U. S. D. A.

Chapter IX

WINTER PASTURE GRASSES

The Rye Grasses.—(*Lolium* Sp.) The Rye grasses are the most popular and useful grasses for temporary or supplemental winter pastures in the South, and deservedly so because they thrive under a wide range of soil and climatic conditions, and will grow with little or no soil preparation. In the South they are used quite often for winter lawns.

Planted in the fall they soon make a carpet of green vegetation and survive freezing weather without injury. The Rye grasses are tender and palatable and make a quick growth in the fall if moisture is plentiful, soon developing a dense turf. If grazed or mowed regularly they produce smaller leaves, and are more desirable than if allowed to go for longer periods.

The Rye grasses grow well in cool weather and for quick fall and winter pastures they are not equalled by any of the other grasses. In the lower South, Italian Rye grass makes a better winter grazing crop than oats. It will produce a good crop when planted on sod land without any soil preparation, provided the turf is not sufficiently dense to prevent the seed from reaching the soil. This is a decided advantage over oats, because the grass may be grazed during rainy periods without injury from trampling when it is planted on unbroken ground.

The Rye grasses prefer a rich soil. They will make satisfactory growth on any well-drained soil that is reasonably fertile, though on poor soils they make a slow growth. They are adapted only to cool weather, and will survive temperatures as low as 10° F. without serious injury. Their range of usefulness is throughout the South, as well as the northern states. They are best adapted for use as a temporary winter and spring grazing crop. They will disappear from permanent pastures in a season or two. Fall plantings are best in the lower South. In the middle or upper South they are very frequently planted in the spring.

The two most important species of Rye grass are Italian Rye grass (*Lolium multiflorum*), and English or perennial Rye grass (*Lolium perenne*). The latter is said to be a biennial or short-lived perennial, but is usually annual in the lower South.

Another species known as Darnel (*Lolium temulentum*), is occasionally found as a pest in grain fields. Darnel is supposed to be the plant referred to as the tares sown by the enemy, in the parable of the tares in Scripture.[1]

Rye grass should be planted in middle fall at the rate of from twenty-five to thirty pounds of seed to the acre. If the seed is sown on turf or unprepared soil a harrow or disk can be used to tear up the turf and allow the seed to get down to the soil to insure quick germination. If rains occur soon after sowing the seed harrowing will not be necessary. On plowed or prepared land the seeds should be lightly covered. In permanent pastures Rye grass will not reseed the land if grazed closely. It is often

[1] George Henslow, *The Plants of the Bible* (London, 1906), p. 119.

used as a nurse crop for clovers on land being started to permanent pasture crops.

Rye grass is used in Europe for both hay and grazing. Perennial Rye grass was one of the first forage grasses to be grown in England, and according to Werner, was cultivated there as early as 1681. It is a native of the Mediterranean countries.

Fig. 46. Rescue Grass. (1) Part of plant showing habit of growth; (2) a single panicle; (3) spikelet much enlarged; (4) a single floret much enlarged. *Courtesy of United States Department of Agriculture.*

Rescue Grass—(*Bromus catharticus.*) Rescue grass deserves a wider use in the South for temporary winter and spring pastures. It is adapted to rich soil with rather mild winters, but it has survived temperatures of the upper South. It is found growing wild in many parts of the lower South, and where the soil is reasonably fertile it stands its own with weeds and other grasses and reseeds from year to year, provided it is not grazed heavily during the seeding stage.

Rescue grass is more desirable for cultivated areas than for permanent pasture plantings. On sod lands, it will

oon disappear under grazing. On cultivated land, how-
ver, it will take the place of small grain to some extent,
nd if conditions are favorable it will afford some grazing
y December. It may be mixed with oats or Rye grass for
all plantings. On poor land it does not make a satis-
actory growth. It makes a good quality of hay, but seeds
nd disappears in the late spring. If allowed to make a
eed crop, it will reproduce itself from year to year from
hattered seed. It usually behaves in the South as a win-
er annual, although it is said to be a perennial.

Rescue grass may be planted in the fall, when fall oats
re sown, on a well-prepared seed bed and lightly cov-
red. From thirty to forty pounds of seed to the acre are
equired to get a good stand of the grass. In mixture with
lover, oats or Rye grass, from ten to fifteen pounds to the
cre would be desirable. Well-drained soil of any nature
hat is sufficiently fertile to grow the small grains will
produce rescue grass. After the grass matures its crop
of seed in the spring, the land can be utilized for summer
rops, and the grass will come to a stand in the fall.

Rescue grass is a bunch grass, and is leafy and pala-
able. It grows erect from two to four feet high with open
panicles sometimes a foot long. It produces seed in abun-
lance and they are of high germination. It is a native
of South America, and is known under various names
ncluding Schrader's grass, Australian brome and Southern chess.

Phalaris.—(*Phalaris angusta.*) This grass is rather
common in the lower South on roadsides and waste places,
where it grows from three to four feet high. It is persistent when once started, and survives on weedy areas.
It has been found growing on all soil types, but where
the soil is fertile it shows a much better growth.

Phalaris seeds from April to June, and the plants die down. The first fall rains cause the seed to germinate and the grass grows through the winter and spring. It is very palatable and is relished by livestock. On rich soil it produces almost as much grazing as oats. Phalaris makes an upright growth under crowded conditions, but if given room and fertility will produce an abundance of succulent forage. On fertile land no soil preparation is necessary. The seed can be broadcast in early fall with good results. Phalaris is best adapted to winter and spring grazing for temporary pasture.

Fig. 47. A Single Plant of *Phalaris angusta.*

Phalaris is an upright winter annual with spike-like panicles produced on stems from two to four feet high. The seed shatter easily and show a high percentage of germination. It should be planted from September to November at the rate of from eight to ten pounds of seed to the acre. It is best adapted to the moist areas of the lower South, and is spreading naturally in waste places of the Gulf Coastal Plains. It is found growing wild in the Gulf States, South Carolina and California.

Chess or Cheat.—(*Bromus secalinus.*) Although considered a pest in wheat fields, chess is of some value for hay and grazing. When planted in the fall it is ready to graze before spring if conditions are favorable. It is a persistent grass in spreading to waste ground and establishing itself among other grasses. However, it will not reseed if grazed closely. It is palatable and makes a good quality of hay, but the yields have not been large. Chess can be utilized where adapted for temporary winter and spring pastures.

Chess is a smooth annual grass growing, usually, three or four feet high. Its introduction into sections where it might become a pest in grain fields is not desirable. It is more hardy to cold than oats, and will grow under less favorable conditions.

Chess begins growth in fall and early winter and matures seed in May and June. Fall plantings require twenty pounds of seed to the acre.

REFERENCES

Alexander, E. D., *Winter Legumes for Georgia,* Extension Bulletin 374, Athens, Ga.

Bailey, R. Y., and Seal, J. L., *Small Grain Crops in Alabama,* Circular 60, Agr. Exp. Sta., Auburn, Ala.

Helm, C. A., *Growing Vetch,* Extension Leaflet 35, Columbia, Mo.

McKee, Roland, and McNair, A. D., *Winter Legumes for Green Manure in the Cotton Belt,* Farmer's Bulletin 1663, U. S. D. A.

Tabor, Paul, *Winter Forage and Cover Crops,* Bulletin 321, Ga. State Col. of Agr., Athens, Ga.

Chapter X

GRASSES USED FOR SOILING CROPS

Napier Grass.—(*Pennisetum purpureum.*) Napier grass promises to be a valuable soiling crop in the lower South. It is a quick growing grass that is cut for green fodder when three or four feet high. At this stage of growth it is palatable and nutritious, and when conditions are favorable several cuttings can be made during the season. Single hills may produce as many as sixty or eighty stems from the crown in a single season. The leaves are abundant and few if any forage plants will grow as rapidly or produce such enormous yields of forage as Napier grass. It has been known to make as much as seven feet of growth in sixty days from established plants cut off at the level of the ground.

Napier grass is an excellent crop for dairy cattle because of its rapid tender growth and high protein content. Green Napier grass contains from 3 to 3½% protein, while the hay contains approximately 11%. If the grass is allowed to get too large the feed value is greatly reduced and the fiber content is high, the stems finally becoming woody and unpalatable.

Napier grass is an excellent soiling crop, and may be cut several times during the season. It does not survive heavy grazing, however, and if grazed closely will dis-ppear from the pasture in two or three seasons. The ields under favorable conditions are very high. Reports ndicate that it will produce more tonnage per unit area han any other forage crop, with the possible exception f Merker grass.

Reports from New outh Wales show yields t the rate of sixteen ons of green fodder per cre from a single cutting. The Agricultural Experiment Station of lorida reports yields s high as sixty tons to he acre on their best nuck lands where the rowing season is long.

Fig. 48. Napier Grass at the Proper Stage of Growth for Use as a Soiling Crop.

Napier grass is best dapted to Florida and he Gulf Coast westvard to Texas; however, it can be grown arther north on fertile oils where moisture is ufficient. Such heavy yields of forage as re produced by this rass require considerable moisture throughout the growing season as well as a ertile soil. Where the temperature drops as low as ten legrees above zero the roots will be considerably injured, nd lower temperatures for long periods may kill it out ntirely. However, it will produce a good yield of green fodder from canes planted each spring. Although Napie grass requires fertile soils for large yields, soils of mod erate fertility produce a fair crop and it will surviv drouths remarkably well. It is adapted to a wide rang of soil types and grows on most soils that produce ordi nary field crops such as corn or Sudan, but the yiel varies with the fertility of the soil. Cultivation is neces sary for Napier grass if good yields are to be expected

Napier grass may be propagated either by portions o the canes, by divisions of the old clumps, or by seed Propagation by seed is practicable in Florida or othe parts of the Gulf Coast. Farther north, in early spring mature canes should be cut in lengths of one or tw joints and placed at three-foot intervals in rows six fee apart and covered with about two inches of soil. At thi rate, there would be approximately 2400 hills to the acre If the seed is used the plants may be started in protecte plats and transplanted to the open field when from si to ten inches high. The blades should be pinched bac when transplanted. On poor soil it should be plante about four feet each way. Seed canes may be cut in th fall before they are injured by frost and placed in "bank" shingle-like and covered with sufficient soil to protec them against the winter weather.

Napier grass is a perennial cane-like plant growing from five to ten feet high or more, depending upon growing conditions. It is a native of tropical Africa, and was introduced into this country by the Department of Agriculture in 1913. Its value was first made known by Colonel Napier of South Africa. It is also known as elephant grass and Napier's fodder. In localities where frosts do not occur before November it matures seed in spikes from four to ten inches long.

Merker Grass.—(*Pennisetum merkeri.*) Merker is losely related to Napier grass and is very much like it n appearance. It produces a large tonnage and requires he same soil and climatic conditions as Napier grass. Merker grass produces seed from early summer to fall, nd its early seeding habits enable it to mature seed arther north than Napier grass, which may make it more lesirable there.

Merker grass grows well from the seed, and will on ertile land produce from the seed a crop of forage from hree to four feet high in ninety days. It is also propagated from the canes by planting them in one or two oint lengths four feet apart in four-foot rows. Merker grass was introduced into the United States by the Department of Agriculture in 1916.

Teosinte.—(*Euchlaena mexicana.*) Teosinte is a succulent tall growing grass requiring fertile moist soil for ts growth. Under ideal conditions it produces as much as fifty tons of green forage to the acre. Teosinte is palatable and nutritious, and produces a large number of stalks from a single hill. It is not widely used, although t is adapted to the entire Cotton Belt.

Teosinte requires a long growing season, and is cultivated the same as corn, its close relative, in four-foot rows spaced three feet in the row. It is propagated from the seed. From three to four pounds of seed should be planted to the acre. It is a native of the tropics, growing from eight to twelve feet high. It is the nearest relative of corn, and crosses readily with it. It is very likely that it was cultivated by the ancient races of Central America.

Guinea Grass.—(*Panicum maximum.*) Guinea grass has been found adapted to conditions in the lower South, near

Fig. 49. Teosinte. (1) Plant showing habit; (2) a branch showing staminate, panicle and fertile ears in axils of leaves; (3) ear; (4) grains; (5 and 6) different views of mature grain. *Courtesy of United States Department of Agriculture.*

the Gulf of Mexico and in Florida. It prefers a heav
rich soil, and has not been found adapted to the ligh
sandy soils. It is not widely used but, where adapted, i
an excellent soiling crop, producing an abundance o

ıtritious forage. It should be cut before it reaches ma-
rity and becomes woody and unpalatable.

On fertile soils where moisture is plentiful, Guinea grass
n be cut several times a year. It is used to some extent
a hay crop in the tropics, but is not well adapted for
is purpose.

Guinea grass is a perennial. It sometimes reaches a
ight of ten feet, with single bunches three or four feet
diameter. It was introduced into the United States
out 1813 and is said to have originally come from
frica as early as 1774, being introduced about that time
to Jamaica.[1]

It is propagated either by seed or root divisions. If
lanted for a soiling crop, it should be planted in rows
om four to six feet apart.

REFERENCES

uggar, J. F., *Southern Forage Crops,* New York, 1925.

iper, Chas. V., *Forage Plants and Their Culture,* New York, 1915.

hompson, J. B., *Napier and Merker Grasses,* Bulletin 153, Agr. Exp. Sta., Gainesville, Fla.

Vilcox, E. V., and Smith, C. B., *Farmer's Cyclopedia of Agriculture,* New York, 1904.

[1] A. S. Hitchcock, *Genera of Grasses of the United States,* De-
artment Bulletin 772, U. S. D. A.

Chapter XI

THE LEGUMES

The legumes, so named because of their pod-like fruit compose one of the most important families of the plant kingdom from an economic standpoint. All legumes are grouped under one large family known botanically as the *Leguminosae.* Taking the rather conservative treatment of Dalla Torre and Harms as a basis, the family *Leguminosae* includes approximately 12,000 species divided among 489 genera. This includes the *Mimosoideae* and *Caesalpinioideae,* regarded as separate families by some authors, notably Britton and Brown in their work on the North American flora.

Of the 489 genera, approximately 135 are restricted to the New World, and 215 to the Old World. The remainder occur in both. More than half of the genera, or about 260, are wholly composed of woody plants not coming under the classification of pasture or forage plants. Approximately 100 are wholly herbaceous, and the rest include plants of both types.

We are primarily concerned with the group making up the valuable pasture and forage plants of the southern states, and those that may become of economic importance for this purpose. The number used for this purpose, while comparatively small, is sufficient to proide varieties adapted to all seasons, soils, purposes and nvironments of this region.

The legume family contains a large number of the most ommon and useful food-producing plants such as the garden peas and beans, and a large number of species used for soil building purposes.

Most of our forage and pasture legumes came from he Old World. It is very evident that Old World plants are more aggressive than our New World species. The ability to occupy the land to the exclusion of other and ess desirable species is a quality that has made many Old World pasture legumes popular in the pasture programs of the South.

Legumes are essential to a balanced pasture and grazing program. They have been recognized for many centuries as soil improving crops. It was not until comparatively recent times, however, that the reason was found for this unusual quality. They are the only group of plants that possess the power to utilize nitrogen from the air and store it in the soil through the formation of root nodules. This is more fully explained in the chapter on inoculation of legumes.

As pastures are grazed and the beef or animal products produced from the pasture are sold or removed from the land, the soil gradually becomes less productive unless fertility is replaced in some way. Legumes keep a proper balance of nitrogen in the soil by taking about as much nitrogen from the air and storing it in the soil through the roots as is removed through the tops by grazing. They contribute to the health of the animals that graze them, as well as to the fertility of the soil, and fortunately many species are available for use as pasture crops that will grow in the winter when grasses and other crops are dead or dormant. They are more resistant to extremes of weather than are the grasses.

The ability of legumes to utilize air nitrogen makes them richer in protein than the grasses. The common pasture legumes contain from 12 to 15% protein, as compared with a 3 to 5% protein content in pasture grasses. Protein is one of the most expensive constituents in the feed of livestock. Legumes supply it in the cheapest form, and the animals harvest it themselves. This latter is necessarily a factor of importance in livestock production.

Animals require considerable lime and phosphorus. These minerals are essential to the normal development of all animals. When it is lacking in the diet of livestock trouble is sure to follow. Creeps, a more or less common ailment of animals in some areas, is traceable to a lack of these minerals. Abortion is often the result of mineral deficiency in the feed. Experimental data are at hand to show that a mineral deficiency in the diet of the mother is reflected unfavorably in the offspring. Legumes supply these necessary minerals in abundance, and no other group of pasture plants can do this. Dairy cattle in milk require a larger proportion of minerals in their diet than cattle not in milk. A high percentage of the solids in milk is made up of lime. Legumes are essential to a balanced pasture program.

REFERENCES

Alexander, E. D., *Winter Legumes for Georgia,* Extension Bulletin 374, Athens, Ga.

Crosby, J. E., Reagan, M. J., and Carter, C. E., *Dairy Pastures,* Extension Circular 271, Columbia, Mo.

Dawson, J. R., *Legume Hays for Milk Production,* Farmer's Bulletin 1573, U. S. D. A.

McKee, Roland, and McNair, A. D., *Winter Legumes for Green Manure,* Farmer's Bulletin 1663, U. S. D. A.

Robinson, B. L., and Fernald, M. L., eds., *Gray's New Manual of Botany,* New York, 1914.

Chapter XII

THE INOCULATION OF LEGUMES

Nitrogen is one of the essential plant foods. Without it plants cannot grow. Many soils are deficient in this valuable element, even though the air is approximately four-fifths nitrogen and holds in suspension above every acre of land, rich or poor, approximately seventy-five million pounds of nitrogen. This vast storehouse of nitrogen which is above and around every living plant is available in its gaseous form to but one family of plants, the legumes.

Under certain conditions these plants are able to take the nitrogen from the air and utilize it in their growth. To make air nitrogen available for these plants, there must be present in the soil certain kinds of bacteria in numbers sufficient to meet the needs of the plants. Where these bacteria are not present, they must be supplied either through artificial cultures or through soil brought from fields where the legumes have successfully grown. Supplying these organisms in either manner is called inoculation.

The fundamental purpose in applying inoculation to the seed of legumes, or to the soil before planting them, is to supply the organisms necessary to the growth of nodules upon the roots of the growing plants.

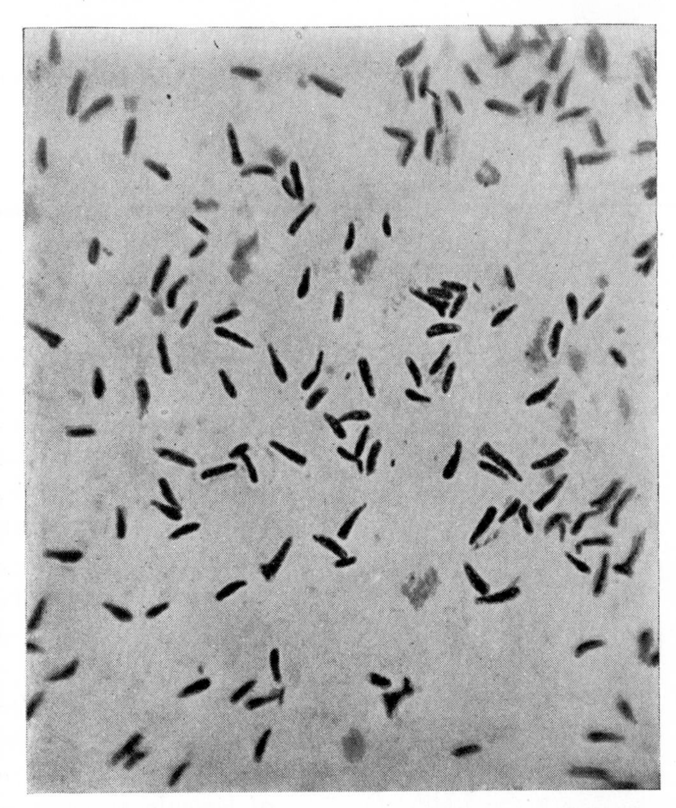

Fig. 50. Nodule Forming Bacteria from Alsike Clover. Greatly Magnified. *Courtesy of United States Department of Agriculture.*

Practical farmers have known for centuries that legumes had the peculiar power of enriching the soils upon which they grew, but they did not know why this was true. Legumes were used in India and China for this purpose ages ago, and the early Romans had some knowledge of the value of legumes over other crops for improving the soil. The reason for this peculiar power of the

Fig. 51. Alfalfa Plant Showing Nodules. *Courtesy of United States Department of Agriculture.*

legume was not known until Hellriegel, in 1887, discovered that the organisms present in the root nodules were responsible for the nitrogen fixation. In 1866, Woronin discovered that the nodules contained bacteria, but their importance was not known at that time. These organisms are known as *Rhizobium*. Professor J. G. Lipman of the New Jersey Agricultural College estimates that the total amount of nitrogen added to the soil in the United States each year from the growth of leguminous crops is equivalent to 1,750,000 tons of nitrogen.

There are only two known methods by which nitrogen is fixed to any extent in nature: First, there are various kinds of organisms that exist in soil or water that account for most of the nitrogen in nature; and, second, electrical discharges in the atmosphere account for a very small amount of nitrogen fixation, but the amount is very small, probably not in excess of two or three pounds to the acre per year. Practically all soils contain bacteria that use decaying vegetable and animal matter as sources for growth and nitrogen fixation. These free-living bacteria do not develop upon the roots of legumes, and their presence in the soil, regardless of conditions, is not sufficient for the successful growth of legumes. They are known as *nonsymbiotic* forms. The legume nodule bacteria, or *symbiotic* forms, are not present in all soils. Where they are not, it is necessary to supply them at the time of planting to insure nodule development on the roots of the plants.

Different Strains of Bacteria.—The quantity of nitrogen fixed in the soil by the various legumes is to a certain extent determined by the kind or strain of organisms used in inoculating the seed, or the type of organism found in the soil. Although nodules may be formed upon the roots, the plant may not be benefited by the work of the bacteria because they do not make nitrogen available for the growing plant. This may account for failures when, apparently, inoculation was successful. It has been observed that legumes inoculated with a strain of bacteria capable of producing nodules were not successful, but later the same variety of legume was successful when inoculated with a different strain of bacteria.

This makes it necessary that plantings be inoculated with cultures that are known to contain the proper strains of bacteria, or that soil from fields or pastures where the same legume has grown successfully be mixed with the seed at the time of planting.

The Importance of Inoculation.—Poor soils are low in organic matter and, consequently, are deficient in nitrogen. Nitrogen is one of the necessary elements for plant growth. Legumes, properly inoculated, are able to produce on soils where the nitrogen content is low, and a shortage of nitrogen does not hinder their growth as would be the case with crops dependent upon the soil for all their supply of nitrogen. Legumes within themselves have no power to utilize the nitrogen of the air except through bacteria that live in the nodules upon the roots. Therefore, it is highly necessary that bacteria of the right strain be present in the soil in sufficient numbers to promote the growth of nodules upon the roots of the plant. The absence of the proper bacteria forces the legume to depend upon the soil nitrogen entirely, as would be the case with non-legumes, and their growth to be governed by the nitrogen which the soil can supply.

Inoculation Improves Feed Value.—Legume crops are high in protein, one of the essential nutrients in feeds for livestock, and the most costly to purchase in concentrates. It is the nitrogen supply in the legume plant that enables it to produce an abundance of protein, making it a forage crop superior to the grasses. If the nitrogen supply is low, the protein content of the plant will be low, and as more nitrogen is made available the plants become richer in protein. Considered from this viewpoint, proper inoculation is essential in the production of feed crops with a high protein content on soils low in nitrogen. Professor W. A. Albrecht of the Missouri College of Agriculture says that, "Hay from soy beans which were not inoculated contained 151 pounds of protein per ton, while the hay from the inoculated crop contained 298 pounds of protein per ton. Inoculation meant a hay richer by 147 pounds of protein per ton."[1] Other legumes will be affected in a similar manner.

Effect of Soil and Climate upon Bacterial Development.—Since nature has provided that the function of bacteria upon the roots of legumes is to supply the growing plants with their nitrogen requirement through nodule development, they are more necessary and hence more active where soil nitrogen is low in content. Experimental data are at hand to show that the development of nodules upon the roots of legumes is much more active when the soil is deficient in nitrogen than when it is plentiful. Poor soils afford suitable environment for the development of legume bacteria and the growth of legume crops, climatic and other conditions being favorable. Experiments with various legumes seem to indicate that nodules do not develop readily as long as the plants can obtain sufficient nitrogen for their growth in the soil. Soils rich in nitrogen will show a vigorous growth of legumes in the absence of nodule bacteria.

Climate has little effect upon the development of nodules upon the roots of the plants, except as it affects their tops and growth. Bacteria on the roots will not usually function properly where the soil is permanently water-logged, or where the soil is crusted or packed to such an extent as to reduce materially the air circulation in the soil. A high moisture content in the soil is favorable to the production of nodules, as long as it is not sufficient to cut off air circulation.

The Amount of Nitrogen in the Tops and Roots of Legumes.—In grazing pastures, considerable of the green forage is removed from the soil in the course of a year. If the fertilizer from the animals is returned to the land,

[1] W. A. Albrecht, *Inoculation of Legumes*, p. 6.

a greater portion of the nitrogen increase from the growth of legumes will be saved. If the fertilizer is not returned, approximately two-thirds of the total nitrogen of the entire plant is taken away with the tops, since about two-thirds of the nitrogen is found in the tops and one-third in the roots. A greater amount is removed by grazing than would be removed if the crops were cut for hay, because a greater total growth results from grazed crops than from crops left ungrazed and cut for hay. Pastures grazed and the livestock removed without returning the fertilizer will just about hold the original nitrogen content, the legumes replacing as much through the roots as is removed by the tops. The amount in the roots represents about the amount supplied by the soil, and the tops the amount supplied by the air through root nodules.

Behavior of Bacteria Toward Leguminous Plants.—The bacteria causing the growth of nodules upon the roots of legumes are extremely small organisms. They are at first rod-shaped with appendages which enable them to move about in the soil. Large forms of the bacteria, variable in shape, may also be found in the same nodules with the rod-shaped ones. Their minute size enables them to enter the roots of legumes through the pores of the root hairs, and to penetrate the soil to considerable depths. They increase very fast where conditions are favorable. A single bacterium may multiply to more than 1,000 millions of its kind in a single day.

Although these organisms resemble each other when viewed under a microscope, their behavior toward legume

---

FIG. 52. Diagram Illustrating the Nitrogen Cycle of a Legume Plant. *Courtesy of Extension Service, United States Department of Agriculture.*

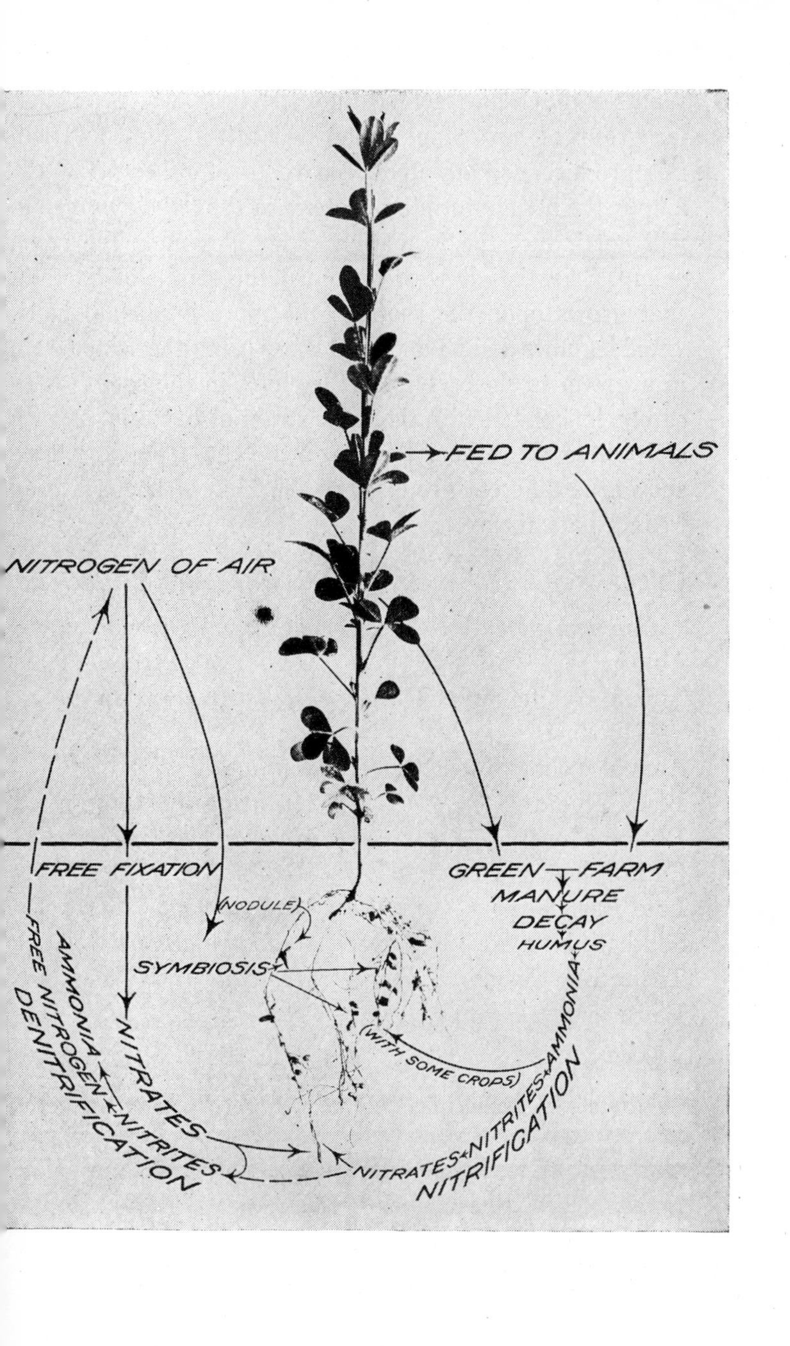
FED TO ANIMALS
NITROGEN OF AIR
FREE FIXATION
(NODULE)
SYMBIOSIS
GREEN
FARM
MANURE
DECAY
HUMUS
(WITH SOME CROPS)
AMMONIA
NITRITES
NITRATES
NITRIFICATION
NITRATES
NITRITES
AMMONIA
FREE NITROGEN
DENITRIFICATION

plants is different. Each strain of bacteria has its particular group of host plants upon which it thrives, and will not produce nodules upon the roots of others. For example, the nodule-forming bacteria of the red clover group will not induce the formation of nodules upon the vetch group. Scientists have determined the strain of bacteria that grows upon the roots of the more important cultivated legumes and have placed those using the same strain in a group to themselves. All legumes in the same group can be inoculated with the same strain of bacteria, or with soil where the others have grown. The following table shows the different groups, and the kind of bacteria used to inoculate them.

GROUP 1.—*Legumes Inoculated with Alfalfa Bacteria.*

Common name	*Scientific name*
Alfalfa	*Medicago sativa*
Annual White Sweet Clover (Hubam)	*Melilotus alba, An.*
Annual Yellow Sweet Clover	*Melilotus indica*
Black Medic	*Medicago lupulina*
Button Clover	*Medicago orbicularis*
California Bur Clover	*Medicago hispida*
Late Bur Clover	*Medicago tuberculata*
Southern Spotted Bur Clover	*Medicago arabica*
Tifton Bur Clover	*Medicago rigidula*
White Sweet Clover	*Melilotus alba, Bi.*
Yellow Sweet Clover	*Melilotus officinalis*

GROUP 2.—*Legumes Inoculated with Red Clover Bacteria.*

Common name	*Scientific name*
Alsike Clover	*Trifolium hybridum*
Buffalo Clover	*Trifolium reflexum*

GROUP 2.—*Legumes Inoculated with Red Clover Bacteria.*—Continued.

Common name	*Scientific name*
Carolina Clover	*Trifolium carolinianum*
Cluster Clover	*Trifolium glomeratum*
Crimson Clover	*Trifolium incarnatum*
Gingin Clover	*Trifolium cernuum*
Little Hop Clover	*Trifolium dubium*
Ladino Clover	*Trifolium repens,* var.
Low Hop Clover	*Trifolium procumbens*
Persian Clover	*Trifolium resupinatum*
Red Clover	*Trifolium pratense*
Strawberry Clover	*Trifolium fragiferum*
Subterranean Clover	*Trifolium subterraneum*
White Dutch Clover	*Trifolium repens*
Yellow Hop Clover	*Trifolium agrarium*

GROUP 3.—*Legumes Inoculated with Vetch Bacteria.*

Common name	*Scientific name*
Austrian Winter Peas	*Pisum arvense*
Broad Bean (Horse Bean)	*Vicia faba*
Canada Field Peas	*Pisum sativum arvense*
Common Vetch	*Vicia sativa*
Garden Pea	*Pisum sativum*
Hairy Vetch	*Vicia villosa*
Lentil	*Lens esculenta*
Narrow Leaf Vetch	*Vicia angustifolia*
Purple Vetch	*Vicia atropurpurea*
Sweet Pea	*Lathyrus odoratus*

GROUP 4.—*Garden and Navy Bean Bacteria.*

Navy beans and common garden beans require the same strain of legume bacteria. This strain is not related to any of the others mentioned above. Garden and navy bean bacteria are present in practically all soils due to the almost universal practice of planting some variety of these two crops.

GROUP 5.—*Lupine Bacteria.*

Common name	*Scientific name*
Blue Lupine	*Lupinus angustifolius*
Serradella	*Ornithopus sativus*
Sundial Lupine (wild)	*Lupinus perennis*
Texas Blue Bonnet	*Lupinus texensis*
Yellow Lupine (European)	*Lupinus luteus*

GROUP 6.—*Cow Pea Bacteria.*

Common name	*Scientific name*
Cow Pea	*Vigna sinensis*
Florida Beggarweed	*Desmodium purpureum*
Jack Bean	*Canavalia ensiformis*
Kudzu	*Pueraria thunbergiana*
Lespedeza (Japan Clover)	*Lespedeza striata*
Lespedeza, Korean	*Lespedeza stipulacea*
Lespedeza (Perennial)	*Lespedeza sericea*
Lima Bean	*Phaseolus lunatus macrocarpus*
Partridge Pea	*Chamaecrista fasciculata*
Peanut	*Arachis hypogaea*
Pigeon Pea	*Cajanus indicus*
Tepary Bean	*Phaseolus acutifolius*
Tick Trefoil	*Desmodium canescens*
Velvet Bean	*Stizolobium deeringianum*

GROUP 7.—*Soy Bean Bacteria.*

The soy bean appears to be in a class by itself as far as legume bacteria are concerned. The bacteria that produce nodules upon the roots of soy beans are not related to any of the other commonly known strains. The soy bean is a native of the Orient, and has been extensively cultivated in the United States for only a comparatively short time. Soils where soy beans have never grown cannot be expected to have the bacteria present. Soy bean seed should always be inoculated before planting to insure proper nodule formation on the roots, unless they have been successfully grown on the same soil before.

Amount of Nitrogen Obtained from the Air.—The amount of nitrogen taken from the air through root nodule development varies with different legumes, and under different soil and climatic conditions. As has already been explained, nodules do not develop readily where nitrogen is plentiful in the soil. Under conditions of this kind less nitrogen is taken from the air than would be the case on soil containing less nitrogen, other conditions being favorable. It is assumed that under conditions favorable to the development of root nodules approximately two-thirds of the nitrogen contained in both the roots and the tops of cultivated clovers is obtained from the air, and one-third from the soil. The amount of nitrogen found in the roots represents approximately the amount taken from the soil by the plants, while that in the tops represents the amount taken from the air.

The Pure Culture Method of Inoculation.—It is apparent that to get full benefits from the growth of legumes, the plants must either find the proper bacteria in the soil to insure the development of root nodules, or they must be supplied through cultures or other means. It has been found possible to isolate nodule-forming bacteria in pure culture. Nobbe and Hiltner of Germany began the production of pure cultures on a commercial scale as early as 1897, and the United States Department of Agriculture began the preparation of pure cultures in 1902. At the present time many of the experiment stations and agricultural colleges supply cultures for the different legumes. Commercial cultures can be obtained from most seed houses in a convenient form, and modern methods of production enable them to be produced at moderate prices. Cultures are usually grown in agar prepared from an Asiatic seaweed, in a nutrient solution, or in sterilized soil, sand or peat. They are mixed with a small quantity of water before they are applied to the seed. After the treatment the seeds are dried in the shade and promptly planted. Artificial cultures have the advantage of being free of objectionable weeds and soil diseases. Most producers of commercial cultures place a date upon the container after which the cultures are not believed to be dependable. Nodule bacteria die out rapidly when allowed to remain dry, and for this reason it is not good practice to store seed after they have been inoculated unless they are to be inoculated again before planting.

Fig. 53. Artificial Inoculation of Alfalfa Seed. *Courtesy of Extension Service, United States Department of Agriculture.*

The Soil Method of Inoculation.—As a means of supplying the proper strain of legume bacteria to new fields, the soil method of inoculation is often employed. Land that has successfully grown legumes with proper nodule development upon the roots will serve as a source of inoculation for other soil that is to be planted to legumes of the same group. Soils to be used for this purpose should be known to be free of undesirable weed seeds and disease-causing organisms. The soil transfer method may result in carrying serious pests and plant diseases to the new fields unless care is used to avoid infested soils. Soil for supplying legume bacteria should be taken only from fields where legumes of the same group as the ones to be inoculated have been growing successfully. If inoculation has been introduced only recently in the soil to be transferred, the bacteria may not have had time to be distributed through the soil by natural growth. An effort should be made to secure soil in which the root nodules have already grown in order to insure an abundance of the nodule-forming bacteria.

Soil to be transferred should be loose and in a condition that will permit it to be handled and distributed with a minimum of time and expense. A half inch of the top crust should be removed and the soil intended for transfer taken from the first four or five inches below that. Unless the transfer soil is to be covered or harrowed into the soil of the new field, sifting is not desirable. On large acreages where plowing or breaking is not practical, small lumps in the transferred soils will give protection to the bacteria contained in them against the direct rays of the sun until rains pulverize the lumps and carry the bacteria down into the soil. Where possible the soil should be transferred just before rains are to occur. If the soil is to be distributed through a fertilizer attachment, it should be sifted through a screen to remove pebbles and lumps. It may be distributed by hand or any other method that will get it evenly distributed over the land to be planted.

Unless the desired kind of soil can be located near the fields to be planted, the soil transfer method is prohibitive. This method, however, is very desirable where the acreage is small and the supply of inoculated soil near at hand. It insures the introduction of the right strains of bacteria, one of the factors that determines the degree of success to be obtained with legumes.

The Glue Method of Inoculation.—This method was first used at the Illinois Experiment Station for the inoculation of large seeds. The soil carrying the legume bacteria is mixed with the batch of seed to be inoculated after the seeds are coated with glue. In this way the soil is transferred along with the seed to the new fields. One objection to this method is the small amount of soil transferred in this manner. A pint of liquid glue is poured over each bushel of seed and stirred until the seeds are uniformly coated with the glue, after which a quart or more of the soil to be used is stirred with the seed until they are coated with it. If the legume bacteria are plentiful in the soil this method will provide satisfactory inoculation. This method is not desirable for small seed.

The Culture Plot Method of Inoculation.—On the large grazing lands of the Gulf Coast and other regions of the South, pasture improvement and the planting of grazing crops presents a different problem from that of the small farm. The improvement of a 15,000-acre pasture is a far different problem from that of a 100-acre pasture. In many instances the seeds are scattered over the surface at intervals and left to take care of themselves. On such vast acreages breaking is out of the question, and soil transfer is not practical. Artificial cultures placed on the seed at the time of planting are subjected to the changing elements and the heat of the sun's rays for days, perhaps, before rains occur to carry the seed down to the soil where they may germinate and begin their growth. Success with legumes under these conditions is hard to attain.

Culture plots, where a few acres of the clovers or legumes to be planted on the large acreage are grown, are the best sources of inoculation for these large acreages. A suitable plot is selected at intervals over the large acreage, properly fertilized, inoculated and planted to the crops desired. In some cases these plots may necessarily have to be fenced and protected against cattle until they are established. After the crops have matured their seed, the top layer of the culture plot soil is transferred to the higher portions of the large acreage. In this way not only are the bacteria transferred to the new soil, but seed from the old are also carried and success is more certain than where other methods are used.

While it will take several seasons to cover a large acreage in this way, it has several advantages. It insures the proper strain of bacteria, enables one to determine the adaptability of the crops to the soils in question and, by transferring the soil to the higher portions of the large acreage, nature aids in spreading the bacteria to lower portions of the land by the drainage water.

REFERENCES

Albrecht, W. A., *Inoculation of Legumes*, Bulletin 282, Agr. Exp. Sta., Columbia, Mo.

Giobel, Gunnar, *The Relation of Soil Nitrogen to Nodule Development, Etc.*, Bulletin 436, Agr. Exp. Sta., New Brunswick, N. J.

Lohnis, F., and Leonard, L. T., *Inoculation of Legumes*, Farmer's Bulletin 1496, U. S. D. A.

Singleton, G. H., *Nitrogen Availability Studies, Etc.*, Bulletin 421, Agr. Exp. Sta., New Brunswick, N. J.

Chapter XIII

THE TRUE CLOVERS

The true clovers are those grouped under the genus *Trifolium*. Many of them are among our most valuable pasture and forage plants. Their range of usefulness makes them popular grazing and hay crops throughout the South. The genus name, *Trifolium,* is from *tres,* three, and *folium,* leaf. The leaves of this group of clovers are mostly palmately trifoliate, that is, the three leaves spread from the same point or apex of the leaf stalk like the outspread fingers of the hand. White Dutch clover is an example of the palmately trifoliate leaf. However, some species of this group have pinnately trifoliate leaves; that is, two of the three leaves are arranged on each side of the leaf stalk a short distance back from the central or third leaf. Low Hop Clover is an example of the pinnately trifoliate leaf. The layman sometimes gets the true clovers with the pinnately trifoliate leaves confused with the medics. A comparison of the blossom and seed pods will quickly settle this point, as the medics are readily distinguishable by the coiled seed pods.

The true clovers are adapted to a wide range of climatic conditions, and species of this group can be found that will thrive in all parts of the South where other pasture plants will grow.

Fig. 54. White Dutch Clover.

White Dutch Clover.—(*Trifolium repens.*) White clover commonly known as White Dutch clover, is the most important winter pasture legume in the South. It is well adapted to sections of the South where moisture is sufficient to sustain it. It is valued chiefly as a grazing plant in mixtures with grasses, and is rarely used alone.

White Dutch clover is found growing wild in all parts of the Cotton Belt, and spreads naturally to grazing lands in areas where it has been introduced. It makes seed profusely throughout its growing season, and often blossoms in midwinter in the lower South when mild winters occur.

White Dutch clover gives grazing over a longer period than any other pasture legume used in the South. After becoming established in pastures, it begins growth with the first fall rains and gives excellent grazing until retarded by winter freezes, being among the first plants to make its appearance in early spring. In the lower South it grows the entire winter. Where the supply of moisture is sufficient, the roots of the plants will survive the summer.

White Dutch clover spreads naturally, and should be included in all permanent pasture mixtures where it is adapted. It does well with Bermuda and Dallis grass, as well as with Kentucky bluegrass and Red Top in the upper South. It grows well in partly shaded areas where moisture is plentiful. It is often found growing in midsummer where protected from the sun.

White Dutch clover is a shallow rooted perennial with solid stems that creep on the surface of the soil and take root at the joints. It mingles with Bermuda and other creeping pasture plants without apparent injury to the clover. In fact, the grasses offer protection to the clover in extremes of temperature. During hot summer weather, the leaves die back to come out again as soon as cool moist weather occurs.

White Dutch clover is best adapted to bottom lands where moisture is reasonably plentiful. Poor dry hillsides do not offer proper conditions for its success. Like most other crops, it does best on fertile soils, but will grow well on any soil that will produce the common pasture grasses. It will grow on acid soils, but will respond to the use of lime.

The seeds are usually planted in the fall, but spring plantings have been known to be successful. It is seldom

Fig. 55. A Field of White Dutch Clover in Bloom, Iberia Livestock Experiment Farm, Jeanerette, Louisiana.

sown alone. A sufficient amount of seed should be used to get a proper balance with other crops, allowing the clover to make up at least one-half of the legumes in the mixture. If too much clover is used the grasses may be shaded to some extent, preventing the formation of a heavy turf so necessary to maximum results from grazing. The seed should be covered very lightly, if at all. A light disking after sowing the seed is necessary where heavy turf prevents the seed from reaching the soil promptly. Very often the seed is sown on the pasture and no further attention given. Where this is done, twice the regular planting requirement of seed should be used to obtain a good stand.

On established pastures, from four to six pounds of seed to the acre will give a good stand. This amount may be planted in the fall from September to November, followed in the spring with Lespedeza for the predominant summer legume. Other clovers are frequently used in combination with White Dutch.

White Dutch clover was probably first used as a pasture plant in England. Its use in Holland where it takes an important place in pasture mixtures, gave rise to the name Dutch clover. It has long been used in European countries, and was early introduced into the United States, being prominently mentioned by writers as early as the latter part of the eighteenth century. It has spread spontaneously to all sections of the United States where moisture is sufficient to sustain it. White Dutch clover is generally supposed to be the shamrock, the national emblem of Ireland, although some authorities say hop clover is the shamrock. It is said that Saint Patrick chose this emblem because the three leaflets to his mind were symbolic of the Trinity.

Fig. 56. Ladino Clover.

"It shines through the bog, through the
brake and the mireland,
And he called it the dear little shamrock
of Ireland."

Good seed germinate under favorable conditions in less than a week. White Dutch clover is a native of Europe.

Ladino Clover.—(*Trifolium repens-latum.*) Ladino clover is a large variety of white clover, somewhat larger than White Dutch. It is less hardy in the lower South, and disappears entirely as soon as hot weather arrives. It is also less cold-resistant than White Dutch, due to its faster and more tender growth.

Ladino clover is used in the irrigated regions of Idaho and on the well watered soils of California, but has not become of any economic importance as a pasture plant in the South. It has been found successful in central Tennessee and northern Virginia. It requires an abundance of moisture and a fertile soil. Under these conditions it produces a large yield of succulent forage that can be cut and fed to poultry and other domestic animals. It will not survive close grazing and trampling by livestock, as the animals eat the prostrate stems and destroy the stand. It has a very shallow root system, and depends upon frequent applications of surface moisture. In the South, Ladino clover makes a luxuriant growth during late fall and early spring, but for some unknown reason rarely survives longer than twelve months. Since the seed is very expensive, plantings are rarely justified. It is one of the most palatable and nutritious forage crops known.

Ladino clover is a native of Europe. It is widely used in Lombardy. It derives its name from Lodi, where it was first extensively used.

Persian Clover.—(*Trifolium resupinatum.*) Persian clover is a species used very largely in Persia and in some parts of northern India for forage. It was introduced into the United States some time before 1912 by the United States Department of Agriculture, and seed was distributed to different parts of the South at that time. No encouraging reports were received on these plantings until about 1925, when it was found to be taking hold in parts of southern Louisiana. Since that time Persian clover has become a popular pasture legume in pasture mixtures for the lower South, and is doing exceptionally well throughout the Gulf Coastal Plain region.

Fig. 57. Persian Clover, Showing Flowers and Seed Pod.

Persian clover is relished by livestock, its hollow stems being tender and succulent and never becoming woody or unpalatable with age. When crowded, the plant grows upright, often reaching a height of two feet if supported. The stems normally fall prostrate on the ground in very much the same manner as bur clover. Its most profitable grazing period is during the spring. While not as persistent under grazing as White Dutch clover, it seeds freely and comes back from its own seed from year to year when once introduced.

Persian clover is a smooth winter annual with small pink flower heads from one-fourth to one-half inch in diameter. The leaves are a little smaller than White Dutch, and a lighter green in color. The stems are smooth and hollow. The velvety seed pods, conspicuous because of their unusual shape, are about one-half inch in diameter and produced in abundance.

Persian clover requires about the same soil conditions as White Dutch. It grows equally well on clay or loamy soils, other conditions being favorable. The seeds germinate in the fall, grow during fall, winter and spring, and mature by early summer. It is adapted to regions with mild moist winters and under such conditions makes sufficient growth during the winter to be of some value as a grazing plant.

Persian clover grows well in mixtures, and is often planted with White Dutch, Bermuda and Dallis grass. It has a deeper root system than White Dutch, and requires less moisture for its success.

The seeds of Persian clover are small and germinate under the same conditions as White Dutch. From four to six pounds to the acre will be required to give a stand. Seed should be planted from September to November and covered very lightly. On pasture lands where a heavy turf of grasses is established, the seed may be sown broadcast and the surface lightly cut with a disk harrow. Successful seedings have been made by broadcasting the seed in early fall and leaving them uncovered. Where the turf is not too dense, the rains will carry a large portion of the seed down to the soil. Twice the normal seed requirement is necessary where this method is used. Seed is produced in Louisiana in commercial quantities. Persian clover is a native of Persia and other Asiatic countries.

Cluster Clover.—(*Trifolium glomeratum.*) Cluster clover, also known as McNeill clover, is a new introduction into the United States. It was first grown in this country by the McNeill Experiment Station in Mississippi, and was first identified as *T. parviflorum,* but later re-identified as *T. glomeratum.* The first planting was made from a few seed found as an impurity in imported White Dutch clover seeds by the Office of Forage Crops of the United States Department of Agriculture. Three plants were secured from this first planting, from which the supply of seed came to give the clover further tests at the McNeill Station.

Cluster clover is similar in appearance to hop clover. The plant branches just above the ground to form a cluster of very fine stems that spread out and lie flat on the ground. Single plants, when not crowded, often form a mass of stems and leaves two feet in diameter. It is a prolific seed bearer. More than one thousand seed heads have been observed on a single plant, and each seed head contains from ten to fifty small seeds. The seeds run around one million to the pound. When crowded, the plant grows erect to a height of from twelve to fifteen inches. The leaves are small and narrow, the blossoms are small and of a pale lavender color.

Cluster clover is apparently adapted to the cut-over pine lands of the Coastal Plains of Mississippi. Experiments so far have failed to justify its use in other parts of the South. The seed germinates in the fall, lives through the winter with rather slow growth and provides grazing from February to June. On soils where it is adapted, it will maintain a stand indefinitely.

Plantings should be made from September to November at the rate of from three to five pounds to the acre. The small seeds sift through the turf and a good stand may be expected without covering. A light disking of the surface on heavy turf lands will aid in getting a more uniform stand, but care should be used to prevent covering the seed too deep.

Little Hop Clover.—(Trifolium dubium.) Little hop clover has been found adapted to such a wide range of soil and climatic conditions that it has taken a prominent place in the list of pasture legumes for southern pastures. This small clover grows on infertile acid soils and, once started in a pasture, soon spreads to other areas.

It makes a poor showing during the winter months, but as soon as warm weather occurs in spring its rapid growth removes every doubt as to whether it is a desirable addition to the grazing lands. It is small like Lespedeza, but survives under trampling and heavy grazing and reseeds under the most adverse circumstances. The small slender stems are always palatable and nutritious, and are produced in abundance during the spring.

Little hop clover is persistent on any soils that will produce the common pasture grasses. It, like other crops, responds to fertility, and will produce more grazing on good soil. However, the stems and leaves of the hop clover plant are always small, and this characteristic is not noticeably affected by differences in soil fertility, the increase in the amount of forage being due to the increase in length and number of the stems or branches.

Little hop clover is a small annual with small stems branching from the base to a length of from six to twelve inches. When closely grazed, the stems lie close to the ground. The leaves are pinnately trifoliate like the medics.

Fig. 58. Little Hop Clover, Showing Flowers and Small Hop-like Seeds.

The flower heads are pale yellow, of a hop-like shape and made up of from eight to twenty flowers.

It is adapted to all soil types of the South that will produce the common pasture grasses and clovers. It survives freezes in the South that completely kill out California bur clover. Temperatures of twenty degrees above zero do not injure it. It is a desirable plant for spring grazing in mixtures with the medics, White Dutch and Persian clovers. The seeds germinate in the fall, and the plants grow slowly during the winter months. They begin to show a good growth by March and furnish grazing until June, when the plants seed and die down, giving Lespedeza and other pasture crops time to develop to the profitable grazing stage.

Little hop clover should be planted from September to November. Spring plantings sometimes do well, but fall seedings are to be preferred. The seed is sown on pasture lands, broadcast at the rate of from three to five pounds to the acre. No covering is necessary unless the turf is dense enough to prevent the seed from sifting through to the soil promptly. Cutting the surface with a disk harrow very lightly is sometimes necessary, but care should be used to prevent covering the seed too deep. It is a native of European countries.

Low Hop Clover.—(*Trifolium procumbens.*) Low hop clover is very similar in appearance to *T. dubium,* but is a little larger and produces a more dense growth of stems and leaves. The flower heads of low hop clover are a bright golden yellow, and are larger than the smaller species, having from thirty to forty flowers in the hop-shaped head. The plant is not readily distinguished from *T. dubium* until the blossoming stage, at which time the golden yellow blossoms are more conspicuous than those of the smaller species.

Low hop clover has no particular advantage over the more common species, except the larger size of the plant, being adapted to the same conditions as *T. dubium.* The same planting requirements as for the smaller hop clover are to be observed. Low hop clover is sometimes called yellow hop clover, but this name rightly belongs to *Trifolium agrarium,* a less common species found from Nova Scotia to Virginia. *T. agrarium* is somewhat upright in its growth, and has palmately trifoliate leaves,[1] that is, all three from the same point, while the low hop, as well as *T. dubium,* has pinnately trifoliate leaves. Low hop clover is a native of European countries.

Subterranean Clover.—(*Trifolium subterraneum.*) Subterranean clover has not taken an important place in pasture programs in the South because it has not been as well adapted to uncultivated lands as some of the other low-growing species. For best results it prefers soils that have recently been cultivated. The large seeds of this variety of clover are also a handicap in seeding pasture lands already sodded to turf-forming grasses.

On soils that produce bur and white clover, subterranean clover can be made a useful grazing crop during spring, and will reseed under favorable conditions.

Subterranean clover is a winter growing annual. During winter the plants make a rather slow growth, but will afford some grazing. Its most useful period is from March to May. During the winter the plants consist only of the leaves and leaf stalks. During this stage of growth it withstands temperatures as low as eighteen degrees above zero without injury. As soon as warm weather arrives the plants put out prostrate runners two or three feet long. These runners form a dense mat of growth from six

[1] B. L. Robinson and M. L. Fernald, eds., *Gray's New Manual of Botany,* p. 509.

Fig. 59. Subterranean Clover. A Dense Mat of Leaves and Stems.

to ten inches deep. The runners do not root at the joint. The plants die as soon as hot weather occurs, usually about June.

Subterranean clover is hairy, and the leaves are similar in appearance to crimson clover. The flower cluster of from three to five ivory-white or pinkish flowers are borne on short stalks or stems that are usually hidden under the mass of leaves. As the bristly seed heads mature they point downward, and very often bury themselves in the soil like the peanut, or anchor in the surface vegetation. The slender prostrate runners are produced in such numbers as to smother out weeds and grasses. Rye grass and rescue grass are not entirely suppressed by it, but heavy stands of the clover would be injurious to pasture plants such as Bermuda unless the clover was grazed systematically.

The seeds of subterranean clover are rather large, being from two to three millimeters in diameter. They will not readily sift through the turf, and when planted on established pasture land from four to six pounds of the seed should be planted to the acre, followed by a light surface breaking with a disk harrow. On lands in a cultivated state where the crop is to supply all the grazing, ten pounds of seed to the acre will be required. It will grow on a wide range of soils, and does best where the rainfall is thirty inches a year or more.

Subterranean clover is a native of Europe, where it has been known for several centuries. Linnaeus described it in 1753. Its use as a pasture plant in the United States followed its introduction into Australia about 1895, and its success there.

Alsike Clover.—(*Trifolium hybridum.*) Alsike clover is frequently used in pasture mixtures in the South. It makes a vigorous growth on permanent pasture lands

ılsike Clover with Timothy. *Courtesy of United States* Fig. 60.
)*epartment of Agriculture.*

where grasses and other crops have already been established, and can be grazed without injury.

Alsike is most valuable in the South for planting on lowlands where other clovers do not make a successful growth. On bottom lands where overflows are common, alsike will prove highly satisfactory. It can be used with any of the common pasture grasses of the South, and its persistent seeding habits will provide for its continuance on the land without the necessity of planting every season.

On poor, dry-natured soils, alsike will not survive the summers. In the lower South it entirely disappears during summer under these conditions. However, on these soils it makes some winter growth and produces good grazing during the spring when moisture is plentiful. On bottom lands, alsike has been known to remain under water for several weeks without being killed. Experiments at the United States Department of Agriculture Experiment grounds, Arlington, Virginia,[2] show that alsike will thrive with the crowns and roots constantly under water.

Alsike clover is widely used with red clover, and with timothy increases the yield and quality of hay.

Alsike is adapted to wet-natured soils. It survives heavy freezes, and if moisture is plentiful will survive during the summer in the South. It can be successfully grown on sour soils, and may be used with other clovers and grasses in permanent pasture mixtures. It is a good crop for sloughs and overflow lands. In the lower South it is recommended for creek bottom lands.

Alsike may be planted directly on the soil without covering from September to November at the rate of from three to six pounds of seed to the acre. If a thick turf of

[2] A. J. Pieters, *Alsike Clover,* Farmer's Bulletin 1151, U. S. D. A.

grasses is established a light surface breaking with a disk harrow will improve the stand.

Alsike clover is a native of Europe. It is also known as Swedish and hybrid clover. It was once thought to be a hybrid between white and red clover, and was named *Trifolium hybridum* by Linnaeus in 1753. Alsike is not a hybrid. It has been grown in Europe for several centuries, but its use in America was not generally known until about 1840, when seed was brought from England for distribution.

Red Clover.—(*Trifolium pratense.*) Red clover is the most important legume grown in America. Over a greater portion of the country it is recognized as a valuable pasture and hay crop. In the northern, central and eastern states red clover makes up a large portion of the cultivated lands. For more than two hundred years it has played an important part in the program of American agriculture as a hay and forage crop, as well as a soil building plant. Red clover has been a prominent pasture and forage plant in Europe for centuries.

Red clover occurs over a greater part of Europe. A large number of varieties have been named by botanists in the Old World, but experiments, as well as the experience of practical farmers in the United States, prove that American varieties are to be preferred for planting. Domestic-grown seed give far better results than imported seed. In fact, the problem in red clover production is largely a problem of seed supply. The mechanical purity of the seed is not enough to insure success with red clover, even though soil and climatic conditions are favorable.

During the two or more centuries that red clover has grown in the United States, distinct strains adapted to our

Fig. 61. Red Clover.

conditions have been developed through selection and natural environment. These varieties are different from, and superior to, European strains. This makes it important to plant only domestic-grown seed.

"At Ames, Iowa, in 1926-27, 296 different lots of imported seed were tested, and in every case the yields fell much below the yields from Iowa seed. In 1927-28 tests were made at the Arlington Experiment farm, Rosslyn, Va., and at North Ridgeville, Ohio. At the Arlington farm, the average yield from 50 lots of imported red-clover seed was 37 per cent of that from domestic seed, while at North Ridgeville 69 imported lots yielded 72 per cent of the yields from domestic seed. Naturally, among these imported lots some were better than others, a few nearly equaling in yield the average from plots seeded to domestic seed. A very large proportion, however, were near failures."[3]

The red clover plant is unable to set seed without external assistance. Bees and other insects aid in pollination. Bumblebees are said to be the most efficient agencies in the pollination of red clover. Where these insects are not plentiful, a short seed crop may be expected.

Red clover is an excellent grazing crop for all livestock. In the South it can be used to advantage in permanent pasture mixtures, although it is not as persistent under grazing as white clover. In permanent pasture mixtures, a pound or two of red clover seed to the acre will improve the grazing and will be well justified if the soil is adapted to its growth.

Red clover develops an extensive root system, often penetrating to a depth of four or five feet. This habit of growth requires a deep soil. Heavy, poorly drained clays are not adapted to its growth. Soils with a liberal supply of rotted vegetation offer proper conditions for red clover. It requires a liberal amount of lime in the soil, and will not grow on strongly acid soils. Applications of barnyard manure will usually answer the lime requirement and make it possible to grow the crop where lime is lacking.

[3] A. J. Pieters, "Red-Clover Problems Turn on Production of Good Domestic Seed," U. S. D. A. *Yearbook, 1930,* p. 451.

Applications of lime may be necessary to get the crop established. Red clover is very exacting in its soil requirements. Fertility plays an important part. Disease-resistant strains have been developed.

Fall seedings are the most successful in the South. When planted in pasture mixtures with other crops, two or three pounds of seed to the acre will be sufficient. Fall plantings in the South usually survive for one season, necessitating plantings every fall. When planted with small grain or alone, from ten to fifteen pounds of seed to the acre will be required. The seed should be covered lightly.

In the states north of the Cotton Belt, red clover is sometimes a perennial, the plants living from three to nine years, but as a rule it does not survive southern summers.

Crimson Clover.—(*Trifolium incarnatum.*) Crimson clover is used for temporary or supplemental pastures on cultivated land in the southeastern states and other parts of the South. It is rarely used in permanent pasture mixtures, not being adapted to this purpose because of its habits of growth. On pasture lands receiving their first plantings, crimson clover can be used to advantage to provide quick grazing and to serve as a nurse crop for the smaller varieties of clover to be used in the permanent plantings.

On soils where it is adapted, crimson clover makes a faster growth than any of the other varieties. When it is planted in September, it will be ready to graze by December. It also makes a rapid growth in early spring.

Crimson clover is frequently used in combination with oats or other fall-sown crops for spring pasture, and its

Fig. 62. Crimson Clover.

value as a soil-improving crop is recognized. It is a valuable clover crop in orchards, and when allowed to make its normal growth and then plowed under is an excellent soil improver, adding considerable nitrogen and humus to the soil. It makes an excellent quality of hay, but should be cut before it has reached maturity. If allowed to reach maturity, the hairy stems and heads may induce the formation of hair balls in the alimentary tracts of horses and mules when used for hay.

Crimson clover makes its best growth on sandy and loamy soils where drainage is good. It will grow on poor soils if moisture is plentiful. Crimson clover grows well in the Gulf Coastal region and other areas in the lower South where the weather is cool and moist during the growing season. It is more tolerant to soils lacking in lime than red clover. It is often planted in corn fields in August and September for winter and early spring grazing, or for plowing under as a green manure crop in the spring. It seeds and dies down at the approach of hot weather in May or June.

Crimson clover is planted from September to November at the rate of from twelve to twenty pounds of clean seed to the acre. The seed should be covered lightly and, if the soil is not moist, the planting should be followed with a drag or cultipacker to hold a sufficient moisture supply to insure a good stand. Unhulled seeds usually give a better stand, but hulled seeds are widely used.

Crimson clover is a winter annual with long narrow and pointed flower heads commonly of a rich scarlet color, though there is also a white blooming, white seeded strain. Crimson clover is a native of Europe, where several different varieties are recognized. It was introduced into America about 1818, and was first used largely as an ornamental plant, later being recognized as a valuable forage plant.

Buffalo Clover.—(*Trifolium reflexum.*) Buffalo clover is found growing wild along the borders of fields and woods both in the upper and lower South. It also grows in the Middle West and along the Atlantic Seaboard, but has not become of any economic importance. It seems to prefer the more fertile soils with a liberal supply of rotted vegetation. Under these conditions it often reaches a height of thirty inches.

Buffalo clover grows through the winter and furnishes fine grazing in the early spring. It produces an abundance of seed, but the germination is poor due to the hard nature of the seed. The seed sometimes remains in the soil three or four years before coming up. Scarifying the seed would eliminate this trouble.

Buffalo clover is an annual or biennial, with a rather upright growth. The large rose-red flower heads turn a golden brown upon drying. The flowers of the head are larger than red clover, being from one-fourth to three-eighths of an inch long, with from twenty to seventy flowers to the head, and from three to five seeds to the pod. It should be planted in the fall at the rate of from ten to twelve pounds of seed to the acre. On rich loamy soils it is worthy of trial.

Carolina Clover.—(*Trifolium carolinianum.*) Carolina clover is of minor importance as a forage plant, although it occurs throughout the South. It resembles White Dutch clover, but is a smaller plant. It furnishes some grazing in the spring, and serves a useful purpose in pastures by inoculating the soil for other species of the *Trifolium* group. It grows on all types of soil where the common pasture grasses grow.

Carolina clover is said to be a perennial, but is an annual in the lower South, coming back in the fall from seed, growing through the winter and spring, maturing its seed either in May or June, and then eventually dying down.

The small heads are white, turning a rusty brown color after the seeds mature. They are smaller than those of

White Dutch clover. It should be planted in the fall at the rate of from three to five pounds of seed to the acre.

Trifolium amphianthum.—This is a winter growing species similar in appearance to White Dutch clover. The seed heads, produced on stems from six to ten inches high, are very much like the White Dutch except that they are a bright rose-red. It has some value as a grazing plant during late winter and spring. It seeds and dies down about May.

This clover produces seed under the soil near the base of the plant, as well as in the heads. It is found in scattered areas throughout eastern Texas, as well as in Louisiana, and some other parts of the South. Little is known of its possibilities, but it is apparently adapted to the same conditions as White Dutch clover.

REFERENCES

Hartwig, H. B., *Seventy-six Clover Questions Answered,* Extension Bulletin 210, Ithaca, N. Y.

Helm, C. A., *Crimson Clover, Etc.,* Extension Leaflet 31, Columbia, Mo.

Kephart, L. W., *Growing Crimson Clover,* Farmer's Bulletin 1142, U. S. D. A.

Kinney, E. J., *Crimson Clover,* Extension Circular 81, Lexington, Ky.

Leidigh, A. H., *Subterranean Clover,* Circular 37, Agr. Exp. Sta., College Station, Texas.

Miller, M. F., and Etheridge, W. C., *How to Grow Red Clover,* Circular 195, Columbia, Mo.

Pieters, A. J., *Alsike Clover,* Farmer's Bulletin 1151, U. S. D. A.

Chapter XIV

ALFALFA AND THE MEDICS

The medics comprise forty or fifty species, most of which are valuable forage plants native to the Mediterranean countries. They have long been recognized as valuable forage plants. Some of them were utilized by the Medes and the Persians centuries ago, and the generic name of this group of legumes is derived from the Greek word, *Medike,* applied to alfalfa by the Greeks because it came to them from Media.

The bur clovers are probably all annuals, and are distributed over a large part of the globe where they have become useful in forage and pasture crop programs. They are distinguished by their burs or pods. There is a wide variation in the size and form of the burs and pods of the medics ranging from the small species, such as *Medicago minima,* to that of snail and button clover. The seed pods of the medics are either one or several seeded, scythe shaped, incurved or variously coiled.

Most of the medics are important forage plants. They require, as a rule, a well-drained soil with a moderate lime content. Acid soils appear not to be adapted to the production of any of the medics utilized for pasture or forage at the present time.

Alfalfa.—(*Medicago sativa.*) Alfalfa is probably the world's most important forage crop. Wherever soils and conditions are adapted to its growth it is being utilized to some extent for this purpose. It has been an important forage crop in Eastern countries for more than twenty centuries. It was widely used by the ancient Persians, and was called *al-facfacah,* "the best crop."

Alfalfa did not come direct to the United States from Europe as did many of our other valuable forage plants, but was introduced into California from Chile in 1854. It is often called Lucerne. This name was probably attached to the plant because of its introduction into the eastern part of the United States from Lucerne, Switzerland.

Alfalfa is very productive on adapted soils. It is valuable for hay, being nutritious and palatable, and makes the largest yield of any standard hay plant grown in this country. It ranks first in hay production in the United States.

Alfalfa has not been utilized extensively for grazing because of the losses of livestock by bloating. It is used for grazing in California, but southern alfalfa fields are used almost entirely for hay, as grazing somewhat injures the stand. If alfalfa is to be grazed, the crop should be allowed to become mature before turning the animals on the crop. This will, to a large measure, eliminate the possibility of injury to the plants as well as reduce the possibilities of bloating.

Animals should be removed early enough in the fall to allow the development of the tops and to insure food reserves in the root systems for wintering over.

The heaviest yields from hay run for from three to seven years, then decline, but the plants often survive much longer than this.

Alfalfa prefers a semi-arid climate. Where the climate

'utting Alfalfa. Spur, Texas. *Courtesy of R. E. Dickson, 'exas Agricultural Experiment Station.* Fig. 63.

is adapted to its growth, it grows on nearly all soil types. In the more humid areas the soil conditions for its growth must be more favorable. The roots penetrate deeply into the soil, and this enables it to survive dry seasons once the plant is established. This habit of growth makes it impossible to produce the crop on soils where the water level is too near the surface.

Alfalfa will not survive where the roots are surrounded by water for any length of time. In regions where the rainfall is over forty inches a year the chances for its success are materially lessened. Deep soils are best suited for the production of alfalfa, for this enables the roots to penetrate to depths that will insure their proper growth.

Heavy applications of lime to the soil are more essential under humid conditions than in regions where the rainfall is under thirty inches, due to the fact that calcium deficiency seldom occurs in regions of low rainfall. However, a liberal lime content of the soil is always essential to the success of alfalfa. If the soils are inclined to be acid, perfect drainage should be established and a liberal supply of lime put on the soil before the production of the crop is undertaken. The amount of lime necessary should be determined by the degree of acidity of the soil, ranging from 2000 to 5000 pounds of agricultural lime per acre.

Fall and spring seeding of alfalfa is practiced in different parts of the country. Spring seeding is common in the irrigated areas of the West. Moisture conditions determine largely whether spring or fall seeding should be attempted. Fall-sown stands may winter-kill in cold climates if the plants do not become thoroughly established before freezing weather occurs. In regions of mild winters, fall seedings are probably the best.

Weeds are a factor in spring plantings in the lower

South, since the crop is frequently smothered out by weeds before the plants become established. The weed problem can be overcome to a large extent by a few cultivations in advance of the planting season to rid the area of weed pests.

The seed should be planted on a well-prepared but firm seed bed. If possible, the land should be prepared sufficiently far in advance to allow the soil to settle and become firm. If this is not convenient, a roller or other implement may be used after the seeds are sown to insure a firm seed bed and an early start of the young plants.

Twenty pounds of seed to the acre are commonly used, and the best authorities on the subject agree that drillings are better than broadcast seedings, although the latter is commonly practiced throughout the South.

The seed should be covered from one-half to two inches in depth, depending upon the soil and the conditions at the time of planting. Alfalfa produces bluish-purple racemed flowers. The seeds are enclosed in twisted or coiled seed pods.

Southern Spotted Bur Clover.—(*Medicago arabica.*) Southern spotted bur clover, also called spotted medic, is the most successful of the bur clover group for Cotton Belt pastures. This is due largely to its ability to survive lower temperatures. If it is planted sufficiently early to allow the plants to become rooted, temperatures of 18° or 20° F. do not injure it. It comes up in the fall, grows through the winter and supplies grazing early in the spring. The grazing period is lengthened in proportion to the earliness of the spring weather. During mild winters it supplies considerable grazing in the lower South.

Southern spotted bur clover grows well in pasture mixtures with other crops, and may well be one of the basic

Fig. 64. Common Alfalfa Planted in 21-inch Rows at Lubbock Texas, Showing a Good Stand and Favorable Growth fo the First Season. *Courtesy of R. E. Karper, Texas Agri- cultural Experiment Station.*

legumes in permanent pasture mixtures with Bermuda and Dallis grass. It survives under heavy grazing and, under ordinary pasture conditions, will reseed itself from year to year.

This clover is sometimes grown in orchards and cotton and corn fields for soil improvement. If it is allowed to mature its seed before it is plowed under it will come up the following fall without reseeding.

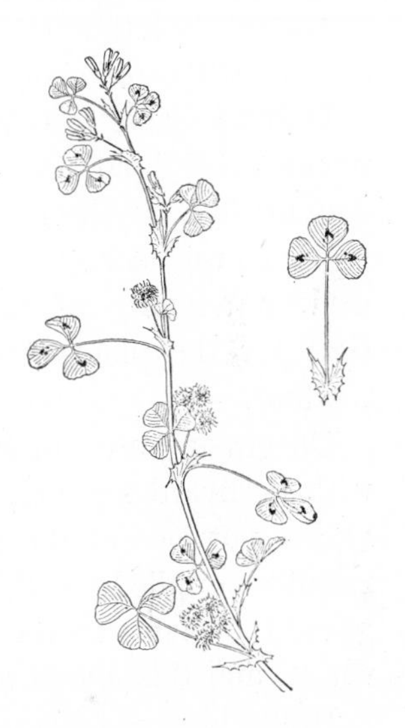

Fig. 65. Southern Spotted Bur Clover. *Courtesy of United States Department of Agriculture.*

It is a good cover crop, and can be utilized with oats and other small grains in temporary pasture mixtures throughout the South. When planted with small grains, it can be utilized for hay. When planted alone, it is not a desirable hay crop because of its low-growing habits.

Southern spotted bur clover grows on all well-drained soils. It is adapted to climatic conditions throughout the Cotton Belt, but is intolerant to strongly acid conditions. Like the other medics, a liberal lime content in the soil improves its growth, though lime is not necessary. This is especially true in the prairie soils of the Gulf Coastal region. It will not produce on water-logged soils.

The seed of this species is usually supplied in the bur. It will require from one to three bushels of the burs to the acre to give a satisfactory stand. One bushel of the burs will be equal to approximately two pounds of hulled seed. The burs may be put out in the spring or summer if they are not to be covered, and this will give time for the decay of the burs and insure quick germination of the seed in the fall. If the burs are planted without covering in the fall, a large percentage of the seed will not germinate until the following year.

It is advisable to cover the burs lightly by disking on uncultivated land. On cultivated areas, they should be covered to a depth of from one-half to one inch, depending upon the character of the soil. They should be planted well in advance of the frost date in order to allow time for the plants to become rooted before the cold weather.

On grazing areas it is a good practice to mix the burs with barnyard manure, scattering this mixture over the higher portions of the grazing lands. In addition to the fertility supplied for the young plants, the cattle do not graze the plants in the manured area as closely as elsewhere, and this allows a larger seed crop.

If the burs are planted in furrows at intervals across the pasture land, the clover will soon spread and cover the area.

Southern spotted bur clover is an annual, producing its seed by June in most sections of the South. It is a native of Europe, and is common in the Mediterranean countries.

California Bur Clover.—(*Medicago hispida.*) California bur clover is common over a wide area of the lower South. It is not as resistant to cold as the spotted variety and, for this reason, has not been a profitable winter legume where the temperature drops as low as 20° F. during the winter. It makes a faster winter growth in the lower South than the spotted variety and, under favorable conditions, is often ready to graze by December 15 from fall plantings.

This is a useful plant in permanent pasture mixtures where adapted, and will reseed under adverse conditions. It is a desirable practice to graze the plant lightly during its seeding stage to insure reseeding of the land.

Like the other medics, this clover prefers well-drained soils and, while lime is not essential, it is beneficial in the production of this crop.

California bur clover is adapted to the same soils as spotted bur clover. Drainage is very necessary. Strongly acid soils will not produce a satisfactory crop of this clover and, where these conditions are found, some other adapted crop should be used in the planting mixture.

Fig. 66. California Bur Clover. *Courtesy of United States Department of Agriculture.*

Hulled seed of this variety can be obtained, and it is rarely necessary to use the burs. Where the burs are used, the same methods of seeding should be used as for southern spotted bur clover. From twenty to thirty pounds of the hulled seed to the acre are necessary where the crop is to be used for soil improvement and for use in orchards and other areas as a cover crop. In pasture mixtures, from two to five pounds of seed to the acre will be sufficient to give a proper balance with the other crops.

Most commercial seeds are scarified and germinate

readily. This has led to the practice of broadcasting the seed over grazing areas without any further attention, but better results will be obtained if the surface is lightly disked after the seeds are sown. Planting should take place as early in the fall as moisture conditions will permit.

California bur clover is a native of Europe.

Black Medic.—(*Medicago lupulina.*) Black medic is a common legume in southern pasture mixtures. It works well in mixtures with other clovers and grasses on grazing lands, and survives heavy grazing exceptionally well. It will reseed under normal grazing conditions but, like the other large seed species, it will be beneficial to the crop if the cattle are removed for a period of time during the seeding stage, in order that a heavy crop of seed may be insured.

Black medic is nutritious and readily eaten by all livestock. The runners of this plant lie close to the soil, enabling it to persist on heavily sodded areas. It is adapted to practically all soil types on which the bur clovers thrive, and is especially well adapted to heavy soil.

Black medic is widely distributed over the South, but it has not become established as thoroughly as some of the other legumes. Its abundance varies greatly from season to season. This probably can be overcome with proper attention to pasture management during the seeding stage of the plant. It is most abundant at the present time on the black prairie soils of Mississippi and Alabama. It is also found in the Gulf Coast region, where it is becoming more popular in pasture mixtures.

Black medic is best adapted to the heavy soils. It does best on the better drained areas and, like the bur clovers, responds to soils which show a liberal lime content. It

Fig. 67. Black Medic. (a) Flowers; (b) Seed Pods.

withstands more cold weather than the bur clovers. It makes a slow growth during winter, but develops fast during the first spring days, affording grazing until late spring. It is a winter annual although occasionally it survives the summer in southern pastures.

In pasture mixtures with other clovers and grasses, from two to three pounds of seed to the acre will give the proper balance. It is rarely planted alone, but may well be mixed with other legumes on adapted soils. If it is the only legume used with grasses, from eight to ten pounds of seed to the acre are required. The seed should be covered lightly, or the turf broken with a disk or harrow so that the seed can reach the soil.

Plantings are usually made from August to November in the lower South. It is common practice in the lower South to sow the seed directly on the sod without further attention. August and September plantings are more desirable in the upper South.

Black medic is a native of Europe. It is also known as yellow trefoil and nonesuch. The flowers are yellow, in short spikes. The seeds are produced in black kidney-shaped pods.

Bur Clovers of Minor Importance

There are several other useful species of bur clovers, there being probably fifty of more or less importance in Europe, with a considerable number that have been found adapted to soil conditions in this country.

Tifton Bur Clover.—(*Medicago rigidula.*) This clover has been used to some extent in southern Georgia. The big burs of this species are one objection to the plant. It is a little more cold-resistant than the other species, but has a larger percentage of stems.

Button Clover.—(*Medicago orbicularis.*) This clover is adapted to practically the same areas as California bur clover, and thrives on the same soil. It is not widely used at the present time, but probably deserves somewhat wider attention.

Snail Clover.—(*Medicago scutellata.*) This species of clover has been found successful upon the same soils as button clover, and thrives under the same conditions.

Medicago minima.—This is a small hairy variety found in parts of the South. Although small it has some desirable qualities, especially its small burs, its resistance to arid conditions, and its ability to withstand cold weather.

There are several spineless varieties. These occasionally are found in plantings of seed of California bur clover. If developed, they would be desirable for grazing lands where sheep are to have the run of the pastures, but the other varieties are so widely established that it would be difficult to use this variety profitably, since the others would probably creep in.

REFERENCES

A Handbook of Agronomy, Extension Bulletin 97, V. P. I., Blacksburg, Va.

Bayles, J. J., *Alfalfa Production Under Irrigation, Etc.,* Bul. No. 472, Agr. Exp. Sta., College Station, Texas.

Garber, R. J., and Odland, T. E., *Varietal Experiments, Etc.,* Bul. No. 250, Agr. Exp. Sta., Morgantown, W. Va.

McKee, Roland, *Button Clover,* Farmer's Bulletin, 730, U. S. D. A.

Piper, C. V., and McKee, Roland, *Bur Clover,* Farmer's Bulletin 693, U. S. D. A.

Chapter XV

THE SWEET CLOVERS

The sweet clovers are included in the genus *Melilotus*. They are all of European origin and are adapted to temperate and subtropical areas. The sweet clovers all have a vanilla-like odor, due to a bitter substance in the sap called coumarin. As the plants advance in age the amount of coumarin in the sap increases and they become less palatable to livestock. In the early stages of their growth the plants contain less of this substance, and livestock will acquire a taste for them more readily if grazing is started while the plants are small.

They have long been recognized as a source of nectar for honey production. The name *Melilotus* is derived from the Greek words, *Meli,* honey, and *lotos,* lotus.

The species of sweet clover common in the United States were once looked upon as noxious weeds, and efforts were made in some sections of the country to eradicate them. However, their persistence prevented this, and they were soon recognized by agronomists as being valuable legumes for both forage and soil-building purposes. Most of the common species produce a good quality hay if cut at the right stage, and are valuable for soil improvement.

All of the cultivated species of this country show a

preference for soil having a high lime content, but their requirements along this line are not as exacting as alfalfa. The United States Department of Agriculture reports that the lime requirement for sweet clover is primarily in the seedling stage of its growth. With this knowledge at hand the production of sweet clover has not been so difficult. It has been found that from four to five hundred pounds of lime to the acre, applied through the drill with the seed at the time of planting, is sufficient on most soils where the supply of lime is low. Late plantings of the summer growing varieties are greatly aided by a supply of nitrogen fertilizers. This gives them an early start and aids them in developing a root system sufficient to care for the plants before the hot dry summer weather occurs.

The sweet clovers have one distinct advantage over most cultivated crops. They are able to utilize the crude forms of phosphorus present in the soil, provided the soil is not too strongly acid. In this manner they convert crude forms of phosphorus into compounds available for succeeding crops. Soils deficient in phosphorus are not adapted to production of sweet clover. Failure of sweet clover on acid soils is due to a lack of lime, the presence of acids, and the unavailability of the locked up phosphates. Lime corrects these conditions. Another advantage of sweet clover is its ability to grow on soil where red clover and alfalfa do not prove successful. This permits the production of hay and forage where conditions are not suitable to red clover and alfalfa.

White Sweet Clover.—(*Melilotus alba.*) White biennial sweet clover is adapted to a wide range of soil and climatic conditions, and will grow with less rainfall than is required for red clover. Like the other species of sweet clover, it shows a decided preference for soils with plenty of lime but, as already stated, this condition can often be corrected by mixing a small quantity of lime with the seed at the time of planting through the drill. White sweet clover is often used in permanent pasture mixtures where legumes are being introduced because it gives quick results and supplies the legumes needed until other adapted crops can become established. It is widely used for dairy pastures as well as for hay. Being a biennial, it supplies grazing and hay for parts of two seasons. In the lower South, fall plantings sometimes go to seed the first year after planting and, for this reason, plantings are usually made in the spring. White biennial sweet clover makes a slow growth in the winter on the average soil, but begins its growth early in the spring and supplies continuous grazing until the new crop is large enough to graze. Two or three cuttings of hay can be secured under favorable conditions. White biennial sweet clover is excellent for honey production, and is probably the best of the sweet clovers with the possible exception of hubam.

White biennial sweet clover is adapted to all sections of the South and withstands the hot sun of the lower South remarkably well, once it is established. It is resistant to cold and survives under winter temperature. It is said to be the best adapted for growth on alkali soils of any of the forage crops. Drainage is essential to the production of white biennial sweet clover. It will not grow on water-logged soil or on land that will overflow for any length of time.

For hay and temporary pasture, from twenty to twenty-five pounds of seed to the acre is the requirement. March plantings are preferred in the South. If unhulled seeds are used, one-third more should be used per acre and they should be planted in mid-winter. White biennial sweet

A Field of White Sweet Clover Grown for Pasture and Hay at Lubbock, Texas. *Courtesy of Texas Agricultural Experiment Station.* Fig. 68.

clover contains a large per cent of hard seed and, for this reason, it is an advantage to have the seed scarified.

White biennial sweet clover is a native of Asia, and was introduced into the United States as early as 1739. It is called by various names, such as Bokhara, white melilot, honey clover, bee clover, galymander and Siberian clover.

Hubam Clover.—(*Melilotus alba,* annua.) Hubam clover is an annual variety of the biennial species. It has come into prominence in the South in recent years because it possesses some advantages over the biennial clover. Among these is its faster growing habit and its ability to produce an abundance of blossoms in three or four months, both of which make it more desirable for honey production. The biennial species requires about fifteen months in producing its crops of flowers.

Hubam is a good soil-building crop, and may be planted in the upper South in the spring. In the lower South it is usually planted in the fall. The soil and seeding requirements are practically the same as for the biennial white sweet clover. It makes a good quality of hay, and is a good grazing plant.

Hubam is said to have originated in Alabama, and was first brought to the attention of the public by a Mr. Hughes of Iowa. The name is a combination of the first syllable of the name of the man who introduced it, and the third syllable of the state in which it originated.

Yellow Sweet Clover.—(*Melilotus officinalis.*) The cultural requirements of the yellow blossom sweet clover are about the same as that required by the white blossom variety. This variety of sweet clover is biennial, and is used quite frequently for hay. It produces a good quality of hay if cut just before the blossoming stage. Later cut-

ubam Clover. The crop is seeding heavily. *Courtesy of* Fig. 69.
exas Agricultural Experiment Station.

Fig. 70. Alfalfa and Sweet Clover; Short Growth of Alfalfa Compared to Sweet Clover, Both in the Bloom Stage. *Courtesy of Texas Agricultural Experiment Station.*

tings allow the plant to advance too far for a good quality of hay, since the stems become woody and less palatable. The leaves often shed badly from cuttings delayed too late in its growth. It is less coarse than the white blossom variety, and is more easily cured on this account. It matures normally about two weeks earlier than the average strain of white blossom sweet clover. Yellow blossom sweet clover makes a rather slow growth during the winter when planted in the fall, but begins growth early in the spring and will afford grazing until the new crop is large enough to graze.

Yellow blossom sweet clover is considered a good

honey-producing plant because of its long-flowering season. For this reason it is frequently used by bee-keepers.

It prefers a soil with a reasonable content of lime, but like the other varieties of sweet clover will often produce on slightly acid soil if four or five hundred pounds of lime are used through the drill with the seed at the time of planting. After it is established its deep rooting habit enables it to withstand dry weather remarkably well, and it will endure the hot sun and cold winters common to the upper and lower South. This species of clover, like others of its group, requires a soil that is well drained. It is an excellent crop for soil improvement. It has been known in European countries for several centuries, and was early used for the production of coumarin for medicinal purposes.

Broadcasting requires from twenty to twenty-five pounds of hulled seed to the acre. The seed should be planted on a firm seed bed and lightly covered. Fall seedings are common, but it produces well from spring plantings. It was introduced from Europe.

Annual Yellow Sweet Clover.—(*Melilotus indica.*) Annual yellow sweet clover, or King Island melilot, is found in waste lands throughout the South, and spreads spontaneously on uncultivated lands along roadsides and railroad rights-of-way. It grows on a great variety of soil types, and is sometimes found on the brackish soil of the better drained portions of the salt grass areas. Annual yellow sweet clover grows off fast in the fall and, because of this habit, is frequently used for both soil improvement in orchards and winter pasturage in the South. It winter-kills more easily than the biennial because of its fast growing habit. On adapted soil it will afford grazing by the middle of December when planted as early as October.

Annual yellow sweet clover is an excellent soil builder, and after the crops have been harvested can be planted to advantage in corn and cotton fields for a green manure crop in the spring. Drainage is essential to the success of this species, but it is more tolerant to excess moisture than other species of this group. It is the most tolerant of acid soils of any of the sweet clovers commonly used in this country.

Annual yellow sweet clover produces on all soils that have sufficient drainage and are not too sour. It is commonly used as a grazing crop for dairy herds. If grazing is started while the plants are young, it will be more palatable and acceptable to the animals. It has been used in rotation with rice and other crops in the lower South and, if allowed to go to seed before it is plowed under, the seed will germinate after the other crops are off the land and give a good stand of clover. It stands its own in grass and weeds, and can be utilized in permanent pasture mixtures to an advantage until other more desirable kinds are established.

Annual yellow sweet clover is planted at the rate of from twenty to twenty-five pounds of seed to the acre, broadcast on a firm seed bed. On lands that have been cultivated during the season no further preparation is necessary. On pasture lands that have become established to grazing, the seed can be sown without cultivation or covering in the fall. It produces seed in April and May and dies down. This species of sweet clover has not been utilized for honey production, probably because of its small blossoms. Only one section has reported the use of it as a honey plant, that being a locality in southern California.

Annual yellow sweet clover is a native of Asia and

European countries. It is sometimes called Indian sweet clover, and sour clover. The name "King Island" was applied to the crop because it was introduced on King Island near Tasmania in 1906 and ultimately led to the establishment of a great dairy industry on that island.[1]

REFERENCES

Coe, H. S., *Sweet Clover; Harvesting and Thrashing the Seed Crop,* Farmer's Bulletin 836, U. S. D. A.

Miller, E. A., *Important Steps in Growing Sweet Clover,* Extension Leaflet 10, College Station, Texas.

Pieters, A. J., *Sweet Clover,* Leaflet 23, U. S. D. A.

[1] Chas. V. Piper, *Forage Plants and Their Culture* (New York, 1931), p. 490.

Chapter XVI

THE LESPEDEZAS

The Lespedezas are not clovers. The name, Japan clover, is commonly applied to common Lespedeza, but it is not a clover and there is no proof that it came from Japan. It is said that the name, Japan clover, was applied to the plant by the botanist, Ravenel.

The name, Lespedeza, was the genus name given to this group of plants by the French botanist, Michaux, who found an American species growing wild in Florida. Some botanical works refer to the Spanish governor of Florida at the time as Lespedez, and indicate that the name was given by Michaux in honor of him, but a search of the records has disclosed that the name of the Spanish governor referred to was Cespedez and not Lespedez.[1] Just how this error occurred is not known.

There are one hundred and twenty-four named species in the genus Lespedeza, seventeen of which are indigenous to the United States. All of the known species are perennials except two, common Lespedeza (*Lespedeza striata*), with its two chief varieties, Tennessee No. 76 and Kobe; and *Lespedeza stipulacea*, or Korean Lespedeza with one extra early variety. *Lespedeza sericea* is the newly introduced perennial species.

[1] A. J. Pieters, *The Little Book of Lespedeza* (Washington, 1934).

Common Lespedeza has been an important forage plant in the South since the Civil War. It was known before this time, but was not widely recognized. Thomas C. Porter collected the first plants of Lespedeza at Monticello, Georgia, in 1846 and sent them to the Gray Herbarium. Just when it came to America is not definitely known.

Lespedeza is one of the best hay plants for the South. It is leafy, with fine stems, and there is little waste. Average figures compiled by the national Bureau of Animal Industry shows a digestible protein content of only 7.9% for Lespedeza as against 11.5% for alfalfa. However, this takes into account the protein alone, which leaves out the starches, sugars and fats. The combined values of the food constituents of a hay are expressed as the digestible carbohydrate equivalent. For Lespedeza, this is 44.8 as against 44 for soy beans, 42 for alfalfa and 37 for cow peas.[2]

The Lespedezas can be used in rotation, as other legumes are used. Korean Lespedeza may be used to advantage as a cover crop in orchards. While Lespedeza responds to fertile soils, it also grows on poor sandy loams, and is tolerant to acid soils.

The weight per bushel of the seed of the different kinds of Lespedeza varies. The table below gives the weight per bushel of unhulled seed, and the number of unhulled seeds per pound as determined from different lots of seed handled by the Division of Forage Crops of the United States Department of Agriculture, and reported in *The Little Book of Lespedeza,* by A. J. Pieters.

Common Lespedeza.—(*Lespedeza striata.*) Lespedeza is the most important summer pasture legume in the South. It is common throughout the southern states, and

[2] A. J. Pieters, *The Little Book of Lespedeza.*

has spread naturally to all the grazing lands where the ordinary pasture plants occur.

	Weight per bushel in pounds		*Approximate number of seeds per pound*
	Unhulled seed	*Hulled seed*	*Unhulled*
Common	28.7	59.4	342,600
Tennessee No. 76	27.7	60.5	342,600
Kobe	30.15	58.7	185,000
Korean	44.6	59.0	240,000

Lespedeza increases the carrying capacity of pasture lands from twenty-five to fifty per cent. This is due more to the food value of the plant than to an increased quantity of forage.

Native Lespedeza is a small plant and does not materially increase the quantity of vegetation growing on pasture lands that are already supplied with plenty of grasses. One distinct advantage of Lespedeza is its ability to crowd into thickly sodded areas and establish itself without thinning out the grasses that are already on the land. Its habits of growth make it especially desirable on Bermuda pastures.

Lespedeza grows on the poor soils, and supplies grazing during the summer and fall months when most other pasture plants are suffering from the hot sun. It shows little preference for soil types, producing upon all the different soils of the South, and is frequently found producing an excellent grazing crop on acid soils. On the average pasture lands of the South, its growth is not

Guernsey Herd on Carpet Grass and Lespedeza Pasture, Richland County, South Carolina. *Courtesy of Extension Service, United States Department of Agriculture.* Fig. 71.

large, ranging from two to six inches in height. Due to this small growth, farmers are sometimes slow to recognize its value.

Lespedeza, being a legume, is very beneficial to the soil where it grows. It survives the hot summer remarkably well throughout the South, and is a desirable pasture plant as far north as the seed will mature.

Common Lespedeza shows a great number of variations. Some effort has been made towards selecting the most desirable types and a great deal of successful work along this line has been done by the Tennessee Agricultural Experiment Station at Knoxville. They have selected several strains that have proved superior in certain ways, the most outstanding example being that of Tennessee No. 76, which has become popular in recent years.

Lespedeza produces its flowers in the axils of the leaves, producing from one to a dozen seeds in clusters. This habit of seeding enables it to survive under heavy grazing because the plant will produce a few seeds even though it is closely grazed, and this is not true of legumes that produce seed at the terminal buds of the stalks. It is a very prolific seed producer, and plants frequently have mature seeds and flowers at the same time.

Lespedeza does well in mixtures with all southern pasture grasses. It will endure a reasonable amount of shade, and this particular habit makes it possible to use Lespedeza with the small grains, thus utilizing the land for grain and summer grazing. Lespedeza is frequently planted in March with fall sown oats and other small grains, and allowed to produce a hay crop after the oats have been cut or grazed down with livestock.

The feeding value of Lespedeza is equal to that of

Fig. 72. Harvesting Lespedeza Seed with a Seed Pan Attached to the Cutter Bar of the Mower. *Courtesy of United States Department of Agriculture.*

alfalfa. It is relished by all livestock, and there is no record of its ever causing bloating.

Lespedeza normally makes a low growth on grazing areas, but it can be used to advantage as a hay crop. For this purpose, it should be planted on fertile land, or it should be fertilized. On good soil it will produce an excellent growth, and will reach a height of from eighteen to thirty inches. The small stems of the plant make it an easily cured hay crop and, in regions where alfalfa cannot be produced, Lespedeza has been found to be an excellent substitute.

The seeds of common Lespedeza shatter easily. This makes it possible to harvest the seed by the use of a seed pan attached to the cutter bar of the mower while the plants are being cut for hay.

Common Lespedeza is adapted to all the pasture land of the South except the poorly drained sections. It will produce upon land where the moisture level is near the surface, but it will not endure standing water for any length of time. It will produce in all parts of the South, though in the upper South it may be more advantageous to use some of the earlier maturing varieties such as Korean. This is especially true where the growing season is short. Lespedeza is sometimes used in partly shaded woodland pastures, and it is a fairly good legume for this purpose.

When planted alone for a hay crop, one bushel of seed to the acre will be required to give a good stand. Seed should be planted on a well-prepared but firm seed bed in February or March, depending upon the earliness of spring weather. As a permanent pasture legume, Lespedeza can well supply one-half of the grazing crops on the lands. This will require that from ten to twelve pounds of seed to the acre be planted. If the land is sodded to grasses, it will be necessary to lightly break or scarify the surface to supply sufficient loose soil for the seed to germinate. Lespedeza seeds germinate very slowly and, if they are planted too late in the season, the stand will be poor unless late spring rains occur. For this reason, it is well to get the seed in the ground and covered before the hot dry weather approaches.

For seed production, a good stand of Lespedeza will yield from five to ten bushels of seed per acre and, occasionally, more. The unhulled seeds weigh approximately twenty-five pounds to the bushel. Fresh seeds show a high germination, the viability of the seed decreasing rapidly with age. Tests at the Tennessee Experiment Station indicate a germination of from 12 to 64% of second year seed.

Korean Lespedeza.—(*Lespedeza stipulacea.*) Korean Lespedeza is a new variety introduced into the United States by the United States Department of Agriculture. It was found growing at Sorai Beach, on the Yellow Sea in Korea, by Dr. Ralph G. Miller in 1919, and the seed was sent to the Department at that time. It was first planted on the trial grounds at Arlington Farms, Rosslyn, Virginia, in 1921, and its value was at once recognized.

The plants of this species are larger and show a faster growth than any other variety of Lespedeza being grown at the present time. In the lower South, Korean produces seed and dies down in July. The seed crop, as a rule, is not very heavy in this region. It is a more desirable crop for the upper South where the seasons are shorter and the sun less severe. The plants of Korean show considerable variation, as is the case with the common Lespedeza, and the Arlington Experiment Farms are attempting to select a variety adapted to areas farther north than any of those being used at the present time. Korean Lespedeza is especially good for the sections with short growing seasons, because it produces its seed crop earlier than the others.

The seed branches of Korean Lespedeza are leafy and dense, and the seeds are produced in the axils of the leaves near the tips of the branches. It produces seed freely, but the seeds do not shatter as easily as that of the common variety, and the hay usually has to be threshed in order to recover all the seed.

Korean Lespedeza is best adapted as a pasture and hay crop in the upper South. It produces on all soil types

Fig. 73. Cattle Grazing Korean Lespedeza, Concord, North Carolina. *Courtesy of United States Department of Agriculture.*

where the common varieties grow, but in producing Korean for hay fertile soil will give a much greater return.

Korean Lespedeza seed should be planted at the rate of from eighteen to twenty pounds of seed to the acre after all danger of frost has passed. The seed should be planted on a well-prepared but firm seed bed, and covered to a depth of one-half inch.

If Korean is used in permanent pasture mixtures, the seed may be planted with other grasses and clovers in the spring, using from three to five pounds of the hulled seed to the acre and using the same methods of seeding as are used for the common varieties. The unhulled seeds weigh about forty-five pounds to the bushel, while the hulled seeds weigh about fifty or sixty pounds to the bushel.

Kobe Lespedeza.—(*Lespedeza striata,* var.) Kobe Lespedeza is a variety of the common species which was brought to the United States from Japan by the United States Department of Agriculture. It is somewhat earlier than common Lespedeza, and produces a larger growth. It shows a spreading habit of growth, but when planted thickly will grow upright and can be utilized as a hay crop.

It produces an abundance of seed, but the seeds are larger than the common variety and it requires a proportionately larger quantity of seed to get a stand. Its growth is two to three times that of the common species.

Kobe Lespedeza is adapted to the same climatic conditions as the common variety and Tennessee No. 76, and its range of usefulness extends through the entire Cotton Belt. It is more drouth resistant than the common variety, being deeper rooted, and starts growth earlier.

Kobe Lespedeza should be planted on a well-prepared seed bed. If it is to be used for hay, from thirty to thirty-five pounds of seed will be required to produce a stand to give a good hay crop. It should be planted in early spring. On permanent pasture lands where Kobe Lespedeza is to be one of the legumes in the planting mixture, from five to ten pounds of seed to the acre will be sufficient.

This variety was found near Kobe, Japan, in 1919 by J. B. Norton, an agricultural explorer of the United States Department of Agriculture. He produced the first seed of it in this country in his garden, and the first seed crop was produced at Hartsville, South Carolina, in 1923.

Tennessee No. 76 Lespedeza.—(*Lespedeza striata,* var.) Tennessee No. 76 Lespedeza is a variety of the common species which was selected at the Tennessee Agricultural Experiment Station from a number of varieties that were tried out at the station. It has several advantages over the common variety. Its habit of growing upright and holding the branches off the ground make it a more desirable hay plant than the common variety. Where adapted, Tennessee No. 76 produces a larger tonnage of hay than the common variety, as a result of its more vigorous growth.

Tennessee No. 76 has become popular in western Tennessee and in parts of North Carolina. Its late seeding habit is the limiting factor in its usefulness farther north.

It is, apparently, adapted to the entire Cotton Belt. If it is to be used for a hay crop, it is well to plant it on productive soils.

One bushel of the unhulled seed to the acre in early spring will be the requirement when seeded alone. From ten to twelve pounds of seed to the acre will be required in permanent pasture mixtures.

Sericea Lespedeza.—(*Lespedeza sericea.*) This is a perennial species introduced into this country by the United States Department of Agriculture in 1924. It was selected from a number of strains obtained in Asia.

The chief advantage of sericea Lespedeza is its value as a hay plant. It produces well on the poorest southern soils, and makes an excellent crop on sour soil. Sericea Lespedeza makes a slow growth on poor soil for the first season but, when once established, it produces an abundance of forage that is relished by all livestock.

It is also an excellent grazing plant and, for this purpose, will probably be best adapted to supplemental pastures. Its value as a permanent pasture legume has not been thoroughly established, but it is apparently adapted to permanent pasture plantings and survives under grazing.

When sericea Lespedeza is once established, the roots penetrate deeply into the soil and it survives periods of drouth exceptionally well. The roots survive the coldest winters, and the plants spread very fast on areas where they are given an opportunity to seed.

The place of sericea Lespedeza in the southern agricultural program is probably that of a hay plant to take the place of alfalfa on poor soils where the cost and uncertainty of producing alfalfa makes it necessary to use some other plant. Sericea Lespedeza grows two or three feet high on the poorest soils and, when once established, will sustain itself.

There are several strains of sericea Lespedeza on the market, two or three of which were distributed by the United States Department of Agriculture. No particular difference in value has been noted between the strains offered the public at the present time.

Fig. 74. *Lespedeza Sericea* Growing on Experimental Farm, College Station, Texas. *Courtesy of Texas Agricultural Experiment Station.*

TABLE IX

Yields of field cured hay, percentage of leafiness, composition and yield of protein per acre of *lespedeza sericea* No. 12087 at Arlington Experiment Farm, 1932.*
(Chemical composition determined by Bureau of Chemistry and Soils, U.S.D.A.)

Plot No.	Date cut	Yield per acre. Air-dry Pounds	% leaves	Composition in Percentage						
				Moisture	Ash	Fat	Crude Protein	Crude Fiber	Nitrogen-free Extract	Protein per acre Pounds
1	6/4	2,032	68.75	6.02	6.17	4.89	18.75	26.46	37.71	381.0
1	7/23	2,687	69.9	6.11	6.07	2.02	14.54	28.93	42.33	390.7
2	6/11	2,674	63.45	6.09	6.28	2.20	16.13	28.40	40.90	431.3
2	8/4	1,795	70.73	5.93	5.77	2.15	12.64	27.40	46.11	226.9
3	6/20	2,993	62.05	6.00	5.75	1.86	14.87	31.57	39.95	445.1
3	8/25	1,824	68.91	5.26	5.75	3.02	12.47	26.32	47.18	227.5
4	6/25	4,163	63.53	6.46	6.10	1.91	14.45	30.69	40.39	601.6
4	9/7	1,663	68.65	5.32	6.04	3.38	11.91	23.95	49.40	198.1

* A. J. Pieters, *The Little Book of Lespedeza.*

Sericea Lespedeza is adapted to the soils of the South. It is a very desirable crop for the hillsides unsuited to the production of alfalfa. On fertile areas, sericea Lespedeza will produce a good hay crop the first season. On poor soil, a light growth can be expected the first year, with an increased amount of forage the second year. The hay and seed crop, however, can both be obtained each year.

Sericea Lespedeza seeds show a poor germination unless they are scarified. Scarified seeds show a high percentage of germination. If it is not possible to procure scarified seed, it is well to sow the seed in the fall to allow the seed coats to become soft so that the seed can germinate in the spring.

It is seeded for hay at the rate of from twenty to twenty-five pounds to the acre from March to May, broadcast on a well-prepared but firm seed bed and covered one-half to one inch deep depending upon the soil texture.

It is sometimes planted in rows and given a little cultivation. Four or five pounds of seed to the acre will be sufficient to give a stand when planted in two-foot or three-foot rows.

The table on p. 219, from *The Little Book of Lespedeza,* by A. J. Pieters, shows the yields of hay, leafiness and composition of sericea Lespedeza.

REFERENCES

Carrier, Lyman, *Lespedeza as a Forage Crop,* Farmer's Bulletin 1143, U. S. D. A.

Essary, S. H., *Lespedeza,* Bulletin 123, and *Three New Varieties of Lespedeza,* Circular 30, Agr. Exp. Sta., Knoxville, Tenn.

Kinney, E. J., and Kenney, Ralph, *Lespedeza in Kentucky*, Extension Circular 179, Lexington, Ky.

Moores, C. A., *Lespedeza Sericea*, Circular 42, Agr. Exp. Sta., Knoxville, Tenn.

Pieters, A. J., *The Little Book of Lespedeza*, Washington, 1934.

Chapter XVII

THE VETCHES

The vetches comprise about one hundred and twenty species. About seventy of these species are perennials; the others are annuals. There are a number of wild species that grow throughout the South. Some of these have value as forage plants, and the cultivated species are among the most important legumes for soil building, forage and hay that we have on southern farms.

The vetches are not used to a great extent in permanent pasture mixtures because of their habit of growth. However, they are of some value when used in this way, provided they are allowed to go to seed. The principal use of vetches, however, is in supplemental or temporary pastures. They are frequently used in connection with the small grains such as rye, oats, wheat or barley for the production of pasturage and hay. Due to their habit of growth, they are seldom used for hay except with a supporting crop.

The cultivated vetches are highly palatable for livestock, and are very rich in protein. They are adapted to a large variety of soils, but inoculation is probably more essential for vetches than with any of the other legumes.

The vetches were among the earliest plants grown for

forage. Reference was made to the culture of vetches for forage as far back as 60 B.C.[1]

Hairy Vetch.—(*Vicia villosa.*) Hairy vetch is a common legume on southern farms, and has been used for soil improvement in Georgia, Alabama and other southern states very successfully. It is a valuable addition to supplemental grazing programs in connection with livestock production in the South.

Hairy vetch can be profitably grown in cotton fields, planted after the crops are harvested in the fall and turned under for green manure in the spring. Or it may be pastured off during the winter and early spring. Like the other vetches, it requires cool weather for growth, and is very resistant to cold.

It prefers a well-drained soil, and produces best on the sandy loams. However, it is frequently grown on other types of soil with good results. It is tolerant to alkaline soils. Many failures with vetch are traceable to a lack of bacterial development on the roots. Inoculation is very essential, and this will have more to do with the success or failure of vetch than the type of soil upon which it is grown.

From thirty to forty pounds of seed to the acre are required where hairy vetch is planted alone. The seed should be planted on a well-prepared seed bed, and covered to a depth of from one-half to one inch, depending upon the type of soil. If planted with small grains in mixture, from fifteen to twenty-five pounds of seed will answer the requirement.

Early fall plantings are to be preferred although spring plantings will frequently give good results in the upper

[1] Chas. V. Piper, *Forage Plants and Their Culture* (New York, 1931), p. 518.

Fig. 75. A Field of Hairy Vetch, in Alabama. *Courtesy of E. Green, Alabama Extension Service.*

South. In the lower South where the summer heat occurs early in the season, spring seedings will not be successful.

Common Vetch.—(*Vicia sativa.*) Common vetch, or tares, requires practically the same soil types and weather conditions as hairy vetch. It is frequently grown as a soil-building crop, as well as a grazing crop in combination with small grains. It makes an excellent hay.

Fig. 76. Common Vetch. *Courtesy of United States Department of Agriculture.*

There are a large number of varieties of common vetch. The most important variety produces gray seeds marbled with a darker color. This variety is also called Oregon winter vetch.

Common vetch prefers sandy loams that are well drained. However, it will produce good crops on most other soil types where water does not stand. It is not as resistant to cold as hairy vetch and, for this reason, is not as common in the upper South for winter use.

When common vetch is planted alone, it will require from fifty to sixty pounds of seed to the acre. When planted with small grains, thirty pounds of seed will be sufficient. It should be planted on a firm seed bed, and covered from one-half to one inch deep, depending upon the soil type. The usual time of seeding is from September to December 1. In the upper South, fall plantings will usually be found best.

Augusta Vetch.—(*Vicia angustifolia.*) Augusta vetch is sometimes called narrow-leaved vetch. It is much earlier than hairy vetch, and is frequently used as a winter crop on meadows where grasses are to be cut or grazed early in the spring and summer. It matures its seed sufficiently early to prevent it from shading or crowding the pasture grasses. It is used to a large extent for hay production, and in combination with small grains on lowlands.

Augusta vetch is a smooth plant with narrow leaves and pinkish-purple flowers. The flowers are usually borne in pairs, and the plant is easily distinguished from common vetch or hairy vetch. It shatters its seed badly, which makes it difficult to harvest but, once started on waste lands, this habit contributes to the spread of the plant.

Augusta vetch is adapted to practically all soil types that are well drained, but prefers the loamy soils. Inoculation is very essential in the production of this, as well as all other vetches.

Augusta vetch should be planted at the rate of from twenty to twenty-five pounds of seed to the acre when planted alone. When planted in combination with small grains, from ten to twelve pounds of seed to the acre will be sufficient. Fall seedings are to be preferred in the lower South. Spring seedings can be used in the upper South. The seed should be covered from one-half to one inch deep.

Purple Vetch.—(*Vicia atropurpurea.*) Purple vetch has become popular in some sections, mainly because it makes a more rapid growth during the winter months than hairy vetch. It is not as resistant to cold weather, however, as hairy vetch, because its rapid growth makes the plants tender. It will survive temperatures as low as 20° F. without material injury.

In the lower South, purple vetch will prove of benefit either alone or in winter mixtures with small grains. It produces larger seeds than hairy vetch and, for this reason, requires from two to three times as much seed to get a stand of the crop.

Fig. 77. Purple Vetch. *Courtesy of United States Department of Agriculture.*

Purple vetch is adapted to the same soil types and conditions as the other varieties. Due to its faster growing habits during the winter, and its sensitiveness to extremely cold weather, it is best adapted to the lower South for winter grazing.

From twenty to twenty-five pounds of seed to the acre is the requirement in combination with small grains for winter pastures. When planted alone, one bushel of seed to the acre will be necessary to get a good stand. The seed should be planted from one-half to one inch deep on a well-prepared seed bed. Fall seedings should take place from September to November in the lower South.

Spring seedings can be practiced successfully in the upper South.

Other Vetches.—Wooly-pod vetch (*Vicia dasycarpa*); Ervil, or black bitter vetch (*Vicia ervillia*); and Hungarian vetch (*Vicia pannonica*) are all of some importance as winter grazing crops.

Ervil has been especially successful in California, and would be well adapted to southern conditions. Wooly-pod makes a little better growth than hairy vetch during the winter. Hungarian vetch appears to be a little more tolerant to poorly drained soils than any of the other varieties.

The same planting requirements should be followed with these as for the other more common vetches.

REFERENCES

Brown, J. B., and Ricks, J. R., *Grasses and Forage Plants,* Extension Bulletin 3, State College, Miss.

Duggar, J. F., *Southern Forage Crops,* New York, 1925.

Helm, C. A., *Growing Vetch,* Extension Leaflet 35, Columbia, Mo.

Piper, C. V., *Forage Plants and Their Culture,* New York, 1914.

Chapter XVIII

PREPARING THE SOIL AND PLANTING THE PASTURE

Pasture crops should never be planted and left upon a loose seed bed. More failures with pasture crops are due to planting on loose seed beds than to any other one cause. In many cases it is necessary to level the land to be planted, and this should always be done where the surface is uneven. Otherwise, the use of the mower in the control of weeds or for cutting the crops for hay is impossible. Where the surface has been plowed, plantings should be delayed until a heavy rain has settled the surface, or the surface should be firmed with a drag or roller. Soil preparation, which includes the breaking of the soil, should be made several weeks in advance of the seed sowing. Seeds of clovers and grasses should be covered lightly. Where the surface is to be firmed down with a roller, seeds sown ahead of the roller are covered sufficiently deep to insure germination under favorable weather conditions.

Pasture lands already growing grasses or clovers may sometimes be seeded to others without the necessity of breaking or turning over the soil. If the sod is sufficiently dense to prevent the small seed from coming in contact with the soil, the surface may be lightly cut with a disk or scratched with a harrow to provide loose soil enough to cover the seed lightly. The first rains will settle the seed to the surface with sufficient soil to cover them. This is the most satisfactory method of introducing new crops in old pastures. This method will be found necessary where a heavy turf of such crops as carpet grass is formed.

Planting seed directly on the unbroken sod is widely practiced on the Gulf Coast. This method is used by cattlemen where large acreages make it impracticable to prepare the surface. More seed is required where this method is used than would be the case where the surface is prepared by scratching lightly. Many of the seeds thus sown germinate in the turf when the first rains occur, and fail to become sufficiently rooted to survive. This method of planting pasture crops has several advantages, however, among them the saving in expense of soil preparation. It also enables the owner to sow his land to the crops desired several weeks ahead of the regular planting season. By planting ahead of the regular time, the seeds have a better chance to settle through the turf and reach the soil before favorable weather for germination takes place.

In wooded sections, trees and underbrush should be removed from pasture lands before seeding is attempted. The best trees should be left for shade, and stumps removed to permit mowing for the control of weeds.

Location of the Permanent Pasture.—Pastures should be located with reference to the best utilization of the land. The location of the pasture will have much to do with the profits derived from it. This is especially true with the dairy farmer. It should be convenient to the barn lot, to shade and to water. The pasture, in addition to the nutrients it furnishes, should be a matter of con-

hade and a Convenient Supply of Pure Drinking Water —Essentials to Livestock Profits. *Courtesy of Extension ervice, United States Department of Agriculture.* Fig. 78.

venience in saving time wherever possible. A pasture in close proximity to the milk barns is essential to high milk production. The production is considerably lowered where a long walk is necessary for the cows to get to and from the pasture.

Selection of Crops for Planting.—Since the pasture is to be an investment that will continue to yield returns over a long period, the initial investment for seed may well be one sufficiently large to give each acre all the seed required to get a good stand of the crops planted. The first investment for seed is all that will be required, except small purchases of seed to keep the stand of grasses and clovers properly balanced over the entire area. Grasses and clovers in pastures should be thought of as crops just as much as corn, cotton or wheat. Plenty of seed should be used.

In selecting crops for pastures, a variety is far better than one or two. Pastures making the best records in the South are usually made up of several grasses and clovers. Grasses should always be supplemented with legumes of some kind. Legumes increase the grazing value of the land, provide phosphorus and lime more abundantly than grasses, and improve the soil upon which they are growing.

Crops should always be chosen so as to include the varieties with similar growing habits, in order that there will be no crowding to result in the extermination of one or more of them on this account.

An important factor in selecting crops for permanent pasture is to arrange for grazing during the different seasons of the year. At least one legume and one grass should be considered in selecting these crops. In most sections of the South dry weather may be expected during some part of the summer. Crops that will survive under these conditions should be included in the mixture. Species that will grow well during fall, winter and spring are also essential to the best results. The purpose in selecting pasture crops should be to provide grazing continuously over as long a period as possible throughout the entire year.

Fertilizing the Pasture.—If pasture crops are to be planted on poor soils, erosion should be stopped by terracing, and fertilizers applied. From one to two hundred pounds of 18% superphosphate to the acre, worked into the surface in early spring, or in the fall if fall crops are planted, will be very beneficial. A complete fertilizer should be applied at the same rate on old soils that have been worn out by continuous cropping. Nitrate of soda, or sulphate of ammonia can be used to stimulate the growth of young seedlings, and to improve the sod. One hundred pounds to the acre will usually be sufficient. Barnyard manure, if well rotted or allowed to heat to kill parasites, is very desirable for pasture crops.

Commercial fertilizers can be best applied with grain drills, or with broadcast fertilizer distributors. They may be applied any time during the growing season, but rains are necessary before much benefit can be expected. On sodded areas the fertilizers may be applied in early spring before the crops begin growth. Disking or harrowing the surface will usually be helpful, but not essential on level areas. On hillsides the fertilizers should be disked into the surface to prevent washing away by surface water during heavy rains. Fertilizers may also be applied with the seed through the grain drill.

Seeding Pasture Lands.—The wheelbarrow type seeder is desirable for clovers and Lespedeza, and can be used in windy weather. Other type seeders, that broadcast the seed, may be used to best advantage on broken or stumpy areas. None of the seeders are very successful with light chaffy seeds such as bluegrass and orchard grass. These usually have to be sown by hand. At the Kentucky Experiment Station grain drills have been used for seeding mixtures containing orchard grass, using the regular grain box instead of the grass seeding attachment. The grain drill handles the seeds successfully through the wheat runs where the volume of seeds to be sown amounts to a half bushel or more to the acre. Reducers can be used where smaller quantities are to be sown. Reducers can be obtained for any make drill.

On large grazing areas, consisting of a thousand or more acres, seeding the land with an airplane is practical and economical. The possibilities along this line were demonstrated by the author in coöperation with a local flying school in 1930 on Gulf Coast prairies. To make this possible, a special seed hopper must be provided, with an outlet through the floor of the ship near the pilot's seat. A slide valve can be used to control the flow of seed, and a ventura provided under the ship at the outlet pipe to form a suction from the propeller blast and scatter the seed. The ship should be flown from twenty to forty feet above the surface of the ground, the altitude somewhat determined by the area covered by the shower of seed.

This method of seeding large acreages will be found practical, but small areas cannot be successfully handled in this manner. Airplanes have been used for scattering forest seeds, dusting cotton and seeding rice, and can be used to introduce new pasture crops on large grazing lands.

In the upper South spring or late winter seedings of

pasture crops will be best when seeded with one of the small grains. The companion crop will help to hold the weeds in check. Most of the pasture grasses of this area, except orchard grass, are best adapted to fall seeding on pastures or meadows where the ground cannot be cultivated lightly. It is often difficult to get a stand of bluegrass from spring seeding. Spring seedings should be done early. To get a stand of grasses or clovers the seeds must be covered, either with an implement or naturally. Seeds that germinate on the surface may be killed by freezes, or die for lack of moisture before they become established. Rains will usually cover grass and clover seeds planted in small grains sufficiently to insure a stand. Where the surface has been "honeycombed" by freezing a good stand is usually certain.

In the lower South the clovers should all be seeded in the fall, with the possible exception of biennial sweet clover, which may be planted either in the fall or spring. The summer growing grasses are usually planted in late February or early March, and the Lespedezas are adapted to spring seeding. The small seeded clovers can be successfully seeded on uncultivated areas without covering the seeds. Where this method of seeding is practiced, twice the usual quantity of seed should be used.

Chapter XIX

PLANTING INFORMATION FOR SOUTHERN STATES

A brief reference to the mixtures adapted to the different southern states is given in the following pages. The mixtures given are suggested as best, and may be changed to suit local community conditions. The amount of seed required will vary according to the crops already growing on the land. It should be borne in mind, however, that plenty of seed should be used, and that the first cost of seeding the pasture is small compared to the returns from the land.

Planting dates for the different crops vary considerably. Full information as to date and rate of seeding is given under the discussion of each crop in another part of this book, to which the reader is referred for further information.

Alabama [1]

The most dependable permanent pasture crops for this state are Bermuda grass, Dallis grass, carpet grass, Red Top, Lespedeza and White Dutch clover. Hop clover will prove valuable where the soil is not too poor. Bermuda may well be the basic plant in all pasture mixtures. Red Top is adapted to the Piedmont Appalachian region and

[1] Information by J. C. Lowry, extension agronomist.

limestone valleys. Black medic is adapted to the Black Land Belt.

Temporary or supplemental pastures may include Sudan grass, soy beans and kudzu for summer, and rye and oats for winter and early spring. Rye grass can be used over most of the state for winter grazing.

The following mixtures are recommended for Alabama:

For general use in all parts of the state:

Imported Dallis grass	10 pounds per acre
Common Lespedeza	10 " " "
Hop clover	1 pound per acre

On the lime soils of the Black Belt:

Imported Dallis grass	10 pounds per acre
Black medic	10 " " "
White Dutch clover	3 " " "

If phosphate is applied to the soil the Dallis grass should be well established before black medic is planted because the black medic plants will grow very vigorously and shade the young Dallis grass plants and prevent them from getting started. On many areas it is not necessary to plant black medic since it is already present and when phosphate is applied it furnishes abundant grazing in the spring. The White Dutch clover should be planted on the bottom land as it does not grow well on the hills.

On the red fertile soils of the Tennessee and Coosa Valleys of northern Alabama where sufficient phosphate and lime are applied:

Kentucky bluegrass	15 pounds per acre
Orchard grass	10 " " "
White Dutch Clover	3 " " "
Common Lespedeza	10 " " "

On moist sandy bottom land in the Sand Mountain area:

Imported Dallis grass	10	pounds	per	acre
Red Top	5	"	"	"
Common Lespedeza	10	"	"	"
Hop clover	1	pound	per	acre

On bottom lands of southern Alabama:

Imported Dallis grass	10	pounds	per	acre
Carpet grass	5	"	"	"
Common Lespedeza	10	"	"	"
Hop clover	1	pound	per	acre

In southern Alabama, on most of the sandy bottom land, carpet grass grows naturally, but Dallis grass is more drouth resistant, grows more erectly, and is probably preferable to carpet grass as a grazing plant. Carpet grass produces an abundance of seed and scatters readily and therefore is very valuable in starting a pasture by furnishing grazing until Dallis grass gets established.

Red Top, orchard grass, Kentucky bluegrass, White Dutch clover, black medic, and hop clover should be planted late in September or early in October. Dallis grass, carpet grass, and Lespedeza should be planted in February or early March. White Dutch clover, black medic, and hop clover should be inoculated.

Arkansas

There are four natural soil divisions in Arkansas that should be considered in attempting the development of permanent pastures: The Lowland section, which extends across the eastern portion of the state; the Coastal Plains section, which occupies most of the southern third of the state; the West Central section, which includes the southern mountainous region; and the North Arkansas section, which includes about two tiers of counties extending across the northern part of the state from Oklahoma to the Lowland section on the east.

Bermuda grass and Lespedeza are adapted to all sections of the state. Carpet grass is confined to the Coastal Plains area, and Dallis grass grows on practically all soils excepting the drier portions of the Coastal Plains region.

Lespedeza and hop clover are the most successful pasture legumes. White Dutch clover, black medic and the bur clovers are also adapted to most localities.

Orchard grass, Kentucky bluegrass and timothy can be grown in the northern part of the state, but are not permanent under heavy grazing.

Sudan grass is adapted to supplemental grazing. Rye grass and rescue grass are adapted to winter and spring grazing, as are the small grains. The common cultivated legumes can be utilized for supplemental or temporary pastures in summer.

D. J. Burleson, extension agronomist, recommends the following mixtures for permanent pastures:

Lowland Section, heavy soils:

Dallis grass	5	pounds per acre
Lespedeza	10	" " "
Red Top	5	" " "
Alsike clover	5	" " "
Black medic	5	" " "

Light soils:

Lespedeza	10	pounds per acre
Dallis grass	5	" " "
White Dutch clover	3	" " "

Coastal Plains Section:

Dallis grass	5 pounds per acre
Carpet grass	5 " " "
Lespedeza	10 " " "

West Central Section:

Dallis grass	5 pounds per acre
Red Top	5 " " "
Orchard grass	5 " " "
Lespedeza	10 " " "

North Arkansas Section:

Orchard grass	15 pounds per acre
Kentucky bluegrass	5 " " "
Alsike clover	5 " " "
Lespedeza	10 " " "

FLORIDA[2]

The commonly used permanent pasture plants in Florida are Bermuda grass, carpet grass, Dallis grass, Bahia grass, centipede grass, para grass, and Lespedeza. Bermuda and carpet grasses do well over practically all the state. Dallis grass is best adapted to the muck or heavy clay lands. Bahia and centipede grasses do well on almost any of the soil types of the state. Para grass is suited only to South Florida. Lespedeza does best on clay lands, or sandy lands underlaid with a clay subsoil reasonably close to the surface.

White Dutch clover does well in rather limited areas such as the muck lands of the Everglades, and some of the so-called flatwoods that have been in cultivation and fertilized and left in a reasonably fertile state.

Sudan grass and cat tail or pearl millet are excellent

[2] Information supplied by W. E. Stokes, Fla. Agr. Exp. Sta.

supplemental pasture plants for summer. Napier and Merker grasses have been found adapted to Florida conditions. Para grass is used to advantage in southern Florida only. It will sometimes winter-kill in the northern part of the state. Rye grass, oats and rye may be used for supplemental winter grazing.

Pasture Mixtures for Florida:

Bermuda grass (from sod)		
Carpet grass	4	pounds per acre
Lespedeza	15	" " "

Dallis grass, 5 pounds, and White Dutch clover, 4 pounds, should be added to the above mixture on the clay and muck soils. Bahia and other grasses mentioned above can be added to advantage where desired.

GEORGIA[3]

A combination of such plants as crimson clover, White Dutch clover, hop clover, bur clover and Rye grass offers the best winter and spring grazing possibilities for permanent pastures in Georgia. Summer pastures should include Bermuda grass, carpet grass, Dallis grass and Lespedeza, the most common and important permanent pasture crops of the state.

Supplemental pastures are essential in Georgia to supply grazing during periods of drouth. Sudan grass and cat tail millet are the most desirable for this purpose. Other crops that can be used for supplemental pastures are the cultivated legumes such as kudzu, cow peas and soy beans during the summer and fall season. Temporary

[3] Paul Tabor and E. D. Alexander, Extension Bulletin 389, Athens, Ga.

pastures for winter can be provided with rye, barley, oats, vetch, crimson clover, Austrian winter peas and Rye grass.

Appalachian Mountain Region.—For rich hilly lands of this area, the following mixture is recommended:

Orchard grass	6	pounds per acre
Meadow fescue	6	" " "
White Dutch clover	3	" " "
Red Top	3	" " "
Kentucky bluegrass	2	" " "
Lespedeza	10	" " "

On the poor soils of this region the orchard grass, Kentucky bluegrass and meadow fescue may be omitted.

Limestone Valley and Upland Region.—Lespedeza and Bermuda grass are the most dependable crops for this region. Where Bermuda is not established, it can be started with sod placed in furrows at intervals of two or three feet. Lespedeza should be planted at the rate of from 15 to 20 pounds to the acre with the Bermuda. Hop clover is desirable for spring grazing.

Cedar Glade region is adapted to the same crops as the Appalachian Mountain region.

Piedmont Region.—For this area, Bermuda grass and Lespedeza are the most dependable, with the addition of bur clover where adapted, White Dutch and hop clover for winter and spring.

Coastal Plain Region.—Centipede grass, Bermuda grass and Lespedeza are best for upland. On the low well-drained areas, carpet grass, Dallis grass and Lespedeza are adapted.

KENTUCKY[4]

Two pasture mixtures are commonly used in Kentucky; one is built around Kentucky bluegrass for the best soils, and the other around Red Top for the poor soils. The most commonly used legumes in pasture mixtures are White Dutch clover and Lespedeza, while red clover is used frequently in the initial seedings on fertile soils. Alsike is used to some extent with Red Top mixtures.

Orchard grass is largely used, and mixed with Lespedeza makes a good pasture. The amount of Lespedeza in pastures in Kentucky will determine largely the carrying capacity of the pasture between the middle of July and the middle of September.

For temporary pasture Sudan grass, sweet clover, red clover, soy beans and cow peas are used. Lespedeza is sometimes used alone for temporary pasture. Korean Lespedeza is adapted to this region.

The following are the rates of seeding pasture crops in Kentucky, as recommended by the Kentucky Agricultural Experiment Station:

Mixture No. 1:

Orchard grass	8	lbs.	per	acre
Lespedeza	3 to 5	lbs.	"	"
Red Top (recleaned)	2	lbs.	"	"
White Dutch clover	½	lb.	"	"

The above mixture is generally useful outside of the Bluegrass Region where considerable permanence is desired. It is also useful in the Bluegrass Region for semi-

[4] Information by E. N. Fergus, Agronomist, Ky. Agr. Exp. Sta., E. J. Kinney, and Ralph Kenny.

permanent pastures. On limed land 3 pounds of sweet clover seed may be added to the mixture.

Mixture No. 2:

Kentucky bluegrass	12 to 15	lbs. per acre
Red Clover	5	lbs. " "
White Dutch clover	½	lb. " "

This is the common mixture sown in starting a bluegrass pasture. Sweet clover may be substituted for the red on limed land or a mixture of the two may be used. Many farmers who do not strip bluegrass seed add 3 or 4 pounds of timothy. On thin land a few pounds of Lespedeza in the mixture will be valuable.

Mixture No. 3:

Timothy	8	lbs. per acre
Red clover	3	lbs. " "
Alsike clover	2	lbs. " "

This is a low-cost temporary pasture mixture for good land. On limed land sweet clover may be substituted for the red and alsike or used in addition to them.

Mixture No. 4:

Red Top (recleaned)	5	lbs. per acre
Lespedeza	3 to 5	lbs. " "

The above mixture is for low, wet lands.

Louisiana[5]

Bermuda grass, Dallis grass and carpet grass are adapted to all parts of the state for summer pasture.

[5] Information by R. H. Lush, La. Agr. Exp. Sta.

These three can be utilized to advantage on most soils of the state, bearing in mind that carpet grass requires a soil with the moisture level near the surface to make its best growth. Lespedeza is by far the best summer legume. Lespedeza seed is produced commercially in this state, and the plant is widely used for hay, as well as for grazing.

White Dutch clover is the best legume for fall, winter and spring grazing. Louisiana is famous for its White Dutch clover, producing much of the commercial seed on the market. The bur clovers, black medic and hop clovers are also adapted to most of the state. The sweet clovers may be used to advantage on fertile or limed soil. Rye grass is the best winter grazing crop for supplemental pastures, and the small grains can be utilized to advantage for this purpose.

Sudan grass is the best supplemental pasture crop for summer. The cultivated legumes, such as soy beans, cow peas and, in late fall, velvet beans can also be used to advantage.

The following planting mixtures can be used in Louisiana:

Coastal Area:

Dallis grass	5	pounds per acre
Carpet grass	5	" " "
Bermuda grass (by sod)		
White Dutch clover	5	" " "
Lespedeza	10	" " "

Cutover Pine Area:

Bermuda grass (by sod)		
Dallis grass	5	pounds per acre
Carpet grass (on lowlands)	5	" " "

Lespedeza	10	pounds	per	acre
Hop clover	2	"	"	"
White Dutch clover	2	"	"	"

Black medic, the bur clovers, hop and Persian clovers can be used to advantage in the Coastal Area mixture, and may be used in other parts of the state. One of the above mixtures will be adapted to other sections, using the Coastal mixture on the low heavy lands, and the other on lighter soils in the hill sections.

MARYLAND[6]

Kentucky bluegrass is used throughout Maryland on the soils of good fertility. On the soils of low fertility orchard grass is commonly used in pasture mixtures for permanent grazing. The two are not recommended together under Maryland conditions because both are equally permanent. Tall meadow oat grass, Red Top, sweet vernal grass, sheep fescue and red fescue are other grasses adapted to permanent pasture conditions. Red Top and alsike clover are favorites for wet lands. English or perennial Rye grass can be used to advantage for quick results, and with timothy establishes itself quickly.

Either Rye grass or timothy will be desirable with alsike clover for the first year, but bluegrass will crowd them out gradually where they are seeded on the same land.

For supplemental pastures Sudan grass is an excellent crop. For supplemental pastures on sweet soils, white sweet clover is largely used. Soy beans can be utilized for this purpose, as can the small grains.

[6] Information supplied by F. W. Oldenburg, extension agronomist.

The following pasture mixtures are recommended for Maryland:

(1) *For heavy soils of good fertility:*

Kentucky bluegrass	5 to 15	pounds per acre
Timothy	10	" " "
or		
English rye grass	10 to 15	" " "
Alsike clover	3	" " "
White Dutch clover	3	" " "

(2) *For heavy soils of low fertility:*

Orchard grass	20	pounds per acre
Timothy	10	" " "
or		
Tall meadow oat grass	14	" " "
Red Top	3	" " "
Alsike clover	4	" " "

(3) *For light loams and sandy soils:*

Orchard grass	14	pounds per acre
Tall meadow oat grass	14	" " "
Red Top	3	" " "
Lespedeza	6	" " "

(4) *For poor soils and gravelly hillsides:*

Orchard grass	10	pounds per acre
Sweet vernal grass	10	" " "
Sheep or red fescue	5	" " "
Tall meadow oat grass	10	" " "
Black medic	5	" " "

Lespedeza can be used in this mixture and sweet clover added where the soil is not sour.

(5) *For wet lands:*

Red Top	10 pounds per acre
Alsike clover	6 " " "

(6) *For supplemental pastures:*

White sweet clover (on sweet soils)	15 pounds per acre
or	
Sudan grass (sown in spring)	20 to 25 " " "

(7) *For early spring pasture:*

Rye	6 pecks per acre

Timothy is usually sown in the fall. The other grasses are sown either in fall or spring with clovers, preferably about the middle of August after making a good seed bed. At this time the entire mixture may be sown. Care must be used not to cover the seed too deep, particularly blue-grass seed which germinates best if left on top of the ground.

Mississippi

The soils of Mississippi are divided into three regions as to pasture crop adaptation: the long leaf pine section; the short leaf pine section, which includes the flat woods, northeast highlands and Pontotoc ridge; and the limestone soils.

In the long leaf area, carpet grass with Lespedeza and White Dutch clover are desirable in the basic mixtures. On the heavier soils, Bermuda and Dallis grass can be added to advantage. In the short leaf area, Lespedeza, White Dutch clover, hop clover, Bermuda grass and carpet grass are adapted. On the limestone soils, black medic, the bur clovers and Dallis grass can be added to the mixture for the short leaf pine area to advantage. McNeill clover and centipede grass have been valuable in the Coastal Plains area, notably around the Coastal Plains Experiment Station at McNeill.

For supplemental pastures, Sudan is the most desirable. Rye grass is excellent for winter and spring grazing. Rescue grass, as well as the small grains, supply good grazing for winter and spring. Sweet clover, the vetches and Austrian winter peas are other crops adapted to supplemental pastures.

The following mixtures are recommended by R. E. Waters, Extension agronomist:

Long Leaf Pine Region:

Carpet grass	10	pounds per acre
Lespedeza	15	" " "
White Dutch clover	3	" " "
Hop clover	2	" " "
Dallis grass	5	" " "

Short Leaf Pine Area:

Bermuda grass (by sod)		
White Dutch clover	3	pounds per acre
Lespedeza	15	" " "
Hop clover	3	" " "
Dallis grass	5	" " "

Limestone Soils:

Bermuda grass (from sod)		
Dallis grass	5	pounds per acre
Lespedeza	15	" " "
White Dutch clover	3	" " "
Hop clover	3	" " "

Black medic	5 pounds per acre
Dallis grass	10 " " "

North Carolina [7]

In the Coastal Plains of North Carolina, Bermuda grass, carpet grass and Dallis grass are the basic crops for permanent pastures. The addition of Lespedeza for summer pastures, and White Dutch clover and alsike clover for the winter mixtures has proved successful.

Red Top is used on the bottom lands and fertile moist soils of the Coastal Plains area. Orchard grass, Kentucky bluegrass and tall oat grass are used in the Piedmont and mountain areas.

The principal crops used for supplemental winter and spring grazing are Rye grass, crimson clover and Abruzzi rye. Wheat, oats and barley are also used to some extent. Sudan and soy beans are the most desirable for supplemental summer pastures.

Small grains and crimson clover are seeded in August or September. Sudan grass and soy beans may be seeded any time from the middle of April to the first of July. Medium early plantings are most desirable.

Recommended pasture mixtures:

1. *Coastal Plain*

(a) For fertile black soils in the Coastal Plain:

Kentucky bluegrass	8 pounds per acre
Red Top	10 " " "

[7] Suggested planting information supplied by P. H. Kime, agronomist, N. C. Agr. Exp. Sta.; E. C. Blair, extension agronomist; and A. C. Kimrey, extension dairyman.

White Dutch clover	4	pounds per acre
Lespedeza	12	" " "

(b) For fertile loamy soils:

Carpet grass	10	pounds per acre
Dallis grass	5	" " "
Kentucky bluegrass	5	" " "
Red Top	5	" " "
White Dutch clover	3	" " "
Lespedeza	12	" " "

(c) For moist sandy soils:

Carpet grass	10	pounds per acre
Dallis grass	5	" " "
Lespedeza	15	" " "

(d) For well drained sandy soils:

Bermuda grass cuttings		
Dallis grass	5	pounds per acre
Lespedeza	15	" " "

2. *Piedmont*

(a) For fertile, well drained soils:

Kentucky bluegrass	4	pounds per acre
Red Top	5	" " "
Orchard grass	8	" " "
Tall oat grass	4	" " "
Dallis grass	4	" " "
White Dutch clover	5	" " "
Alsike clover	2	" " "
Lespedeza	8	" " "

(b) For fertile, moist soils:

Kentucky bluegrass	4	pounds per acre
Red Top	5	" " "
Orchard grass	8	" " "
Dallis grass	4	" " "

White Dutch clover	5	pounds per acre
Lespedeza	10	" " "

(c) For moist soils in lower Piedmont:

Carpet grass	8	pounds per acre
Dallis grass	4	" " "
Red Top	5	" " "
White Dutch clover	3	" " "
Lespedeza	15	" " "

(d) For poor, dry soils:

Bermuda grass from cuttings		
Dallis grass	5	pounds per acre
Lespedeza	15	" " "

3. *Mountains*

(a) For fertile, well drained soils:

Kentucky bluegrass	5	pounds per acre
Red Top	5	" " "
Orchard grass	8	" " "
Tall oat grass	8	" " "
Timothy	5	" " "
White Dutch clover	2	" " "
Alsike clover	2	" " "
Lespedeza	5	" " "

(b) For moist fertile soils:

Kentucky bluegrass	5	pounds per acre
Red Top	6	" " "
Orchard grass	8	" " "
Timothy	2	" " "
White Dutch clover	3	" " "
Lespedeza	6	" " "

Oklahoma

In Oklahoma, Bermuda grass is probably the best grass as a basic plant for permanent pasture, especially in the cotton areas. Orchard grass, Red Top, Kentucky bluegrass and timothy are all adapted to a small area in the northeastern part of the state. The bur clovers and hop clovers are well adapted to the southern Ozark region, and to practically all of the southeastern part of the state. Lespedeza makes its best growth in the eastern half of the state. Dallis grass appears to be adapted to all of southeastern Oklahoma, although there is some doubt as to its ability to survive the winter weather sufficiently to make it a dependable pasture plant. In the "Panhandle," as well as in much of the western half of the state, Buffalo grass and blue grass make up a large portion of the grazing. The bluestems are important grazing plants in all except the extreme western part of the state, and in the Panhandle.

For supplemental or temporary pastures, Sudan grass is by far the best. Sweet clover is also very desirable. Johnson grass can be utilized for grazing where it is established.

Planting mixtures for Oklahoma have been recommended by Professor B. F. Kiltz of the Oklahoma A. & M. College, as follows:

For the bluegrass region:

Red Top	8 to 10	pounds	per	acre
Orchard grass	12 to 20	"	"	"
Kentucky bluegrass	14 to 18	"	"	"
Timothy	10 to 12	"	"	"

For the Bermuda grass region:

Bermuda grass (from sod)	
Lespedeza	10 pounds per acre
Dallis grass	5 to 10 pounds per acre

Legumes should always be added to the pasture mixture.

South Carolina

South Carolina is divided into three distinct soil regions, as far as pasture crops are concerned: (1) the Coastal Plains section, consisting mainly of Norfolk and Portsmouth sandy soil; (2) the Pee Dee section, which is mostly a sandy soil; and, (3) the Piedmont section, consisting of Cecil and Davidson series of clay soils.

Bermuda grass is the basic grass for permanent pastures in all sections of the state. Dallis grass, carpet grass and Red Top may be added where desired. Lespedeza is the best summer legume for permanent pastures. White Dutch clover, the bur clovers and sweet clover are also adapted to this state in pasture mixtures.

Sudan grass is the most desirable supplemental pasture crop for summer. Alfalfa, sweet clover, red clover and crimson clover are adapted to the Piedmont region. To make these crops successful, it is generally necessary to apply a ton of limestone per acre, and to increase the humus content of the soil by plowing under vegetable matter or cover crops. Inoculation should always be practiced on soils where clovers have not successfully grown.

S. L. Jeffords, Extension Agronomist, recommends the following planting mixtures for South Carolina:

Piedmont Good Uplands and Hillsides:

Bermuda grass from cuttings				
Dallis grass	8	pounds	per	acre
Lespedeza	25	"	"	"
White Dutch clover	6	"	"	"
Bur clover	10	"	"	"

On the poor uplands, Lespedeza and Bermuda grass are most desirable.

On the moist bottom lands, Red Top, 10 pounds, and carpet grass, 10 pounds, may be substituted to advantage in the above mixture for bur clover.

Coastal Plains Dry Sandy Lands:

Bermuda grass from cuttings	
Lespedeza	25 pounds per acre

On moist or bottom lands, carpet grass and White Dutch clover should be added.

Tennessee

Red clover will grow on the more fertile soils in all parts of Tennessee. Red Top is adapted to the poorer types of soil. On more fertile soil timothy, Red Top and red clover are adapted. Kentucky bluegrass and orchard grass are adapted in upper east Tennessee and the Central Basin section of middle Tennessee. West Tennessee is outside the bluegrass area. Lespedeza is grown extensively in western and middle Tennessee, and is spreading rapidly over East Tennessee. It is adapted to all the state. Alfalfa can be grown in most of the state by the application of lime and phosphate, and barnyard manure on the poorer soils. Lime is essential to the production of profitable red clover and alfalfa crops on most all soils of the state. Tennessee resistant red clover is recommended for all parts of the state where red clover grows.

The Tennessee permanent pasture mixture is as follows: [8]

1. Two years Lespedeza, and rye and vetch sowed in the fall after the Lespedeza has matured seed.
2. Lime and inoculate some time during the two years.
3. Sow in the fall,

Orchard grass	8	pounds	per	acre
Red Top	2	"	"	"
Kentucky bluegrass	2	"	"	"
Alfalfa	2	"	"	"
White Dutch clover	2	"	"	"
Sweet clover (in spring)	6	"	"	"
Lespedeza (following spring)	6	"	"	"

Lespedeza should be included in all pasture mixtures. For supplemental pasture, and hay, Sudan grass, soy beans and other cultivated legumes may be relied upon.

Texas

The state of Texas has a wide variety of soil types and climate. In the western portion of the state, permanent pasture development will have to consist largely in utilizing the native vegetation to the best advantage. Good management with alternate grazing will aid in this region. The native grasses of this region consist largely of curly

[8] Supplied by R. H. Milton, extension agronomist.

mesquite grass, buffalo grass, and the Gramma grasses, in addition to a number of wild vetches and wild peas.

Bermuda grass is the most important pasture grass of the rest of the state. Dallis and carpet grasses are adapted to a wide area in the eastern and southern parts of the state, since they are best suited to the moist lands.

Hop clover, White Dutch clover and Lespedeza grow throughout the eastern half of the state. Black medic, the bur clovers and sweet clovers do well on the blacklands and calcareous alluvial soils of the eastern part of the state, and Persian clover has been very successful in the Gulf Coastal prairies where the land is well drained.

Sudan grass is the best supplemental summer pasture grass. Alfalfa and sweet clover can be used to advantage for this purpose where adapted, as can the commonly cultivated legumes.

Rye grass and rescue grass are very successful on the fertile soils of the entire eastern and central portion of the state for winter and early spring grazing. The small grains can also be used to advantage for this purpose. The following planting mixtures are adapted to Texas conditions.

East Texas Timbered Area:

Bermuda grass (by sod)		
Dallis grass	5	pounds per acre
Carpet grass (on moist land)	5	" " "
White Dutch clover	3	" " "
Hop clover	2	" " "
Lespedeza	10	" " "

Bur clover and medic can be added to advantage on fertile soils.

Gulf Coastal Prairies:

Bermuda grass (by sod)	
Dallis grass	5 pounds per acre
Carpet grass	4 " " "
Lespedeza	10 " " "
White Dutch clover	5 " " "

Persian clover, bur clover, hop clover and black medic can be used in this area, and will improve the grazing.

Blackland Belt:

Bermuda grass (by sod)	
Dallis grass	10 pounds per acre
Black medic	5 " " "
Bur clover	5 " " "
Buffalo grass (by sod)	

Virginia

For the southern portion of Virginia best results are obtained from orchard grass, Red Top, red clover, White Dutch clover, sheep fescue and Lespedeza. Orchard grass is the basis of the mixtures, and the other grasses are varied according to the soil type.

Sweet clover is also quite an important pasture crop for this section. It is used in permanent pastures by rotating the pastures and allowing the sweet clover to get one season's growth before grazing. This gives an abundance of grazing the second year.

Lespedeza gives a good growth during the hot summer period when other pasture grasses are at their lowest stage of development, and is an excellent means of tiding over the slack midsummer grazing perod. Sudan grass is adapted to supplemental pasture plantings.

Abruzzi rye is used in this state as a winter grazing crop with excellent results. Other small grains can be utilized to advantage. Red clover, alfalfa, White Dutch clover, alsike, sweet clover, hairy vetch and soy beans are adapted to all sections of the state. Austrian winter peas, Lespedeza and crimson clover are adapted to the eastern half.

Pasture mixtures recommended by the V. P. I. Agronomy Department are as follows:

Strong loams and clay soils:

Kentucky bluegrass	10	pounds	per	acre
Red Top	3	"	"	"
Orchard Grass	10	"	"	"
Alsike clover	3	"	"	"
Red clover or alfalfa	3	"	"	"

Light loam or sandy soils:

Tall meadow oat grass	8	pounds	per	acre
Orchard grass	10	"	"	"
Red Top	3	"	"	"
Red clover	6	"	"	"
Lespedeza	12	"	"	"

Wet bottom lands:

Red Top	3	pounds	per	acre
Meadow fescue	12	"	"	"
Alsike clover	5	"	"	"
Timothy	8	"	"	"

Poor land and gullied hillsides:

Sheep fescue	6	pounds	per	acre
Red Top	3	"	"	"

Orchard grass	10 pounds per acre
Lespedeza	10 " " "
Alsike	3 " " "

Bermuda grass—about a bushel of chopped roots.

West Virginia[9]

Many pasture areas of this state are too steep or rough to make soil preparation practicable for planting permanent pastures. Some of these that are too rough for plowing may be improved by harrowing where possible, and by addition of lime and fertilizers. Nearly all soils in the state may be benefited by applications of lime. White Dutch clover, alsike, red clover and Lespedeza are good pasture legumes for this state. White sweet clover is used on limed soil. Kentucky bluegrass, timothy and orchard grass are used on productive soils, while tall meadow oat grass and Canada bluegrass are well adapted to the poor soils.

On many farms of the state rotation grazing may be practiced profitably. This is common in the eastern and northern Panhandle.

Rye and vetch are excellent crops for fall planting for early spring grazing. The sweet clovers are often added to this mixture for summer grazing.

Sudan grass is the most desirable temporary pasture crop, while sweet clover produces well for midsummer and fall.

The following pasture mixtures are recommended for this state:

[9] Information supplied by T. E. Odland, R. J. Garber and D. R. Dodd of the W. Va. Agr. Exp. Sta.

For productive soils with a hay crop preceding pasture:

Timothy	6 pounds per acre
Red clover	6 " " "
Kentucky bluegrass	4 " " "
Orchard grass	2 " " "
White Dutch clover	2 " " "

For productive soils with no hay crop preceding pasture:

Kentucky bluegrass	10 pounds per acre
Timothy	4 " " "
Orchard grass	2 " " "
Alsike clover *	2 " " "
White Dutch clover	2 " " "

For poor soils with a hay crop preceding pasture:

Orchard grass	8 pounds per acre
Tall meadow oat grass	8 " " "
Alsike clover	4 " " "
Canada bluegrass	4 " " "
Red Top	2 " " "
White Dutch clover †	2 " " "

For poor soils with no hay crop preceding pasture:

Canada bluegrass	10 pounds per acre
Tall meadow oat grass	6 " " "
Orchard grass	6 " " "
Red Top	2 " " "
Alsike clover *	2 " " "
White Dutch clover †	2 " " "

* On limed soil 4 pounds white sweet clover may be used instead of the Alsike.

† Lespedeza may be substituted for part of the White Dutch clover in these mixtures.

Index